WeightWatchers®
PointsPlus®

# POWER FOODS
## COOKBOOK

**ASIAN BAKED KABOCHA SQUASH, PAGE 274**

**WeightWatchers®**
PointsPlus®

# POWER FOODS
## COOKBOOK

### 200 SIMPLE & SATISFYING RECIPES

**AMARANTH "POLENTA"
WITH LEEKS AND SHIITAKES,
PAGE 221**

# About
# WeightWatchers®

Weight Watchers International, Inc. is the world's leading provider of weight-management services, operating globally through a network of company-owned and franchise operations. Weight Watchers holds nearly 50,000 weekly meetings worldwide, at which members receive group support and education about healthful eating patterns, behavior modification, and physical activity. Weight-loss and weight-management results vary by individual. We recommend that you attend Weight Watchers meetings to benefit from the supportive environment you find there and follow the comprehensive Weight Watchers program, which includes a food plan, an activity plan, and a behavioral component. In addition, Weight Watchers offers a wide range of products, publications, and programs for people interested in weight loss and weight control. For the Weight Watchers meeting nearest you, call **1-800-651-6000**. For information about bringing Weight Watchers to your workplace, call **1-800-8AT-WORK**. Also visit us at our Web site, **WeightWatchers.com**, and look for **Weight Watchers Magazine** at your newsstand or in your meeting room.

# Weight Watchers Publishing Group

VP, Editorial Director **Nancy Gagliardi**

Creative Director **Ed Melnitsky**

Photo Director **Deborah Hardt**

Managing Editor **Van Sias**

Editorial Assistant **Katerina Gkionis**

Food Editor **Eileen Runyan**

Editor **Jackie Mills, R. D.**

Recipe Developers **Debbie Goldsmith, Paul Piccuito, Sarah Reynolds, Miriam Rubin, Mark Scarbrough, Bruce Weinstein**

Production Manager **Alan Biederman**

Photographer **Romulo Yanes**

Food Stylist **Anne Disrude**

Prop Stylist **Amy Elise Wilson**

Designer **Gary Tooth, Empire Design Studio**

Illustrations **Mara Cespon**

Front cover: Spicy Tofu Stir-Fry with Broccolini and
Cashews (page 178). Back cover: Cheddar and Vegetable
Frittata (page 44), Cheese and Black Bean Nachos (page 50),
Grilled Flank Steak with Tomato-Fennel Salad (page 63).

# Contents

# About Our Recipes

While losing weight isn't only about what you eat, Weight Watchers realizes the critical role it plays in your success and overall good health. That's why our philosophy is to offer great-tasting, easy recipes that are nutritious as well as delicious. We make every attempt to use wholesome ingredients and to ensure that our recipes fall within the recommendations of the U.S. Dietary Guidelines for Americans for a diet that promotes health and reduces the risk for disease. If you have special dietary needs, consult with your health-care professional for advice on a diet that is best for you, then adapt these recipes to meet your specific nutritional needs.

To achieve these good-health goals and get the maximum satisfaction from the foods you eat, we suggest you keep the following information in mind while preparing our recipes:

### THE PROGRAM AND GOOD NUTRITION

● Recipes in this book have been developed for Weight Watchers members who are following the *PointsPlus* program. *PointsPlus* values are given for each recipe. They're assigned based on the amount of protein (grams), carbohydrates (grams), fat (grams), and fiber (grams) contained in a single serving of a recipe.

● Recipes include approximate nutritional information; they are analyzed for Calories (Cal), Total Fat, Saturated Fat (Sat Fat), Trans Fat, Cholesterol (Chol), Sodium (Sod), Carbohydrates (Carb), Sugar, Dietary Fiber (Fib), Protein (Prot), and Calcium (Calc). The nutritional values are calculated by registered dietitians, using nutrition analysis software.

● Substitutions made to the ingredients will alter the per-serving nutritional information and may affect the *PointsPlus* value.

● Our recipes meet Weight Watchers Good Health Guidelines for eating lean proteins and fiber-rich whole grains, and having at least five servings of vegetables and fruits and  two servings of low-fat or fat-free dairy products a day, while limiting your intake of saturated fat, sugar, and sodium.

● Health agencies recommend limiting sodium intake. To stay in line with this recommendation we keep sodium levels in our recipes reasonably low; to boost flavor, we often include fresh herbs or a squeeze of citrus instead of salt. If you don't have to restrict your sodium, feel free to add a touch more salt as desired.

● In the recipes, a green triangle (▲) indicates Weight Watchers® Power Foods.

● FYI serving suggestions have a *PointsPlus* value of 0 unless otherwise stated.

● Recipes that work with the Simply Filling technique are listed on page 319. Find more details about this technique at your meeting.

● For information about the science behind lasting weight loss and more, please visit **WeightWatchers.com/science**.

All *PointsPlus* values in this book are for one serving.

### CALCULATIONS NOT WHAT YOU EXPECTED?

● You might expect some of the *PointsPlus* values in this book to be lower when some of the foods they're made from, such as fruits and vegetables, have no *PointsPlus* values. Fruit and most veggies have no *PointsPlus* values when served as a snack or part of a meal, like a cup of berries with a sandwich. But if these foods are part of a recipe, their fiber and nutrient content are incorporated into the recipe calculations. These nutrients can affect the *PointsPlus* values.

● Alcohol is included in our *PointsPlus* calculations. Because alcohol information is generally not included on nutrition labels, it's not an option to include when using the hand calculator or the online calculator. But since we use alcohol information that we get from our nutritionists you might notice discrepancies between the *PointsPlus* values you see in our recipes, and the values you get using the calculator. The *PointsPlus* values listed for our recipes are the most accurate values.

## SHOPPING FOR INGREDIENTS

As you learn to eat healthier and add more Weight Watchers Power Foods to your meals, remember these tips for choosing foods wisely:

**Lean Meats and Poultry** Purchase lean meats and poultry, and trim them of all visible fat before cooking. When poultry is cooked with the skin on, we recommend removing the skin before eating. Nutritional information for recipes that include meat, poultry, and fish is based on cooked, skinless boneless portions (unless otherwise stated), with the fat trimmed.

**Seafood** Whenever possible, our recipes call for seafood that is sustainable and deemed the most healthful for human consumption so that your choice of seafood is not only good for the oceans but also good for you. For more information about the best seafood choices and to download a pocket guide, go to **environmentaldefensefund.org** or **montereybayaquarium. org.** For information about mercury and seafood go to **Weight Watchers.com**.

**Produce** For best flavor, maximum nutrient content, and the lowest prices, buy fresh, local produce, such as vegetables, leafy greens, and fruits in season. Rinse them thoroughly before using and keep a supply of cut-up vegetables and fruits in your refrigerator for convenient, healthy snacks.

**Whole Grains** Explore your market for whole-grain products such as whole wheat and whole-grain breads and pastas, brown rice, bulgur, barley, cornmeal, whole wheat couscous, oats, and quinoa to enjoy with your meals.

## PREPARATION AND MEASURING

**Read the Recipe** Take a couple of minutes to read through the ingredients and directions before you start to prepare a recipe. This will prevent you from discovering midway through that you don't have an important ingredient or that a recipe requires several hours of marinating. And it's also a good idea to assemble all ingredients and utensils within easy reach before you begin a recipe.

**Weighing and Measuring** The success of any recipe depends on accurate weighing and measuring. The effectiveness of the Weight Watchers program and the accuracy of the nutritional analysis depend on correct measuring as well. Use the following techniques:

- Weigh food such as meat, poultry, and fish on a food scale.

- To measure liquids, use a standard glass or plastic measuring cup placed on a level surface. For amounts less than $1/4$ cup, use standard measuring spoons.

- To measure dry ingredients, use metal or plastic measuring cups that come in $1/4$-, $1/3$-, $1/2$-, and 1-cup sizes. Fill the appropriate cup and level it with the flat edge of a knife or spatula. For amounts less than $1/4$ cup, use standard measuring spoons.

# Eggs

Breakfasts,
Brunches, and
Lunches

# Eggs

## YOU NEED

1 to 2 servings per day of lean protein; 2 to 3 eggs counts as 1 serving.

## WHY THEY'RE ESSENTIAL

**Eggs are a smart start to your day.** Eating breakfast with a high-quality protein like eggs helps sustain your energy throughout the morning.

**Make a meal that's full of goodness.** Eggs have 13 essential vitamins and minerals, unsaturated fats (the good kind), and antioxidants. They're also one of the best food sources of naturally occurring vitamin D.

**Egg on!** A single large egg contains 6 grams of protein and is considered a complete protein because it contains the 9 essential amino acids needed by the body for building muscle and for tissue repair.

## WHAT TO BUY

**Whole Eggs:** Buy eggs in a store that keeps them under refrigeration at all times; if they're stored at room temperature, shop at another store. Always open the container to check for cracked or broken eggs; eggs should be clean. Check the sell-by date. Eggs will keep for about 3 weeks in the refrigerator past the sell-by date.

*TIP: Most recipes for baked goods call for large eggs, so this is the most practical size to buy; though for scrambling, boiling, or poaching, size does not matter.*

Here's a guide to the types of eggs you'll find in most supermarkets.

REGULAR EGGS: Hens are kept in light- and temperature-controlled cages and fed a diet of grains.

CAGE-FREE EGGS: Hens are allowed to roam in a barn or building with unlimited access to food and water.

FREE-RANGE EGGS: Hens live outdoors or have access to the outdoors. They have a diet of grains, but may also eat plants and insects outdoors.

ORGANIC EGGS: Hens are fed a diet that is grown organically, without using pesticides, herbicides, or fertilizers.

OMEGA-3 EGGS: Hens are fed a diet supplemented with fish oil and flaxseeds, which are high in omega-3 fatty acids.

**Refrigerated Egg Substitute:** Check the ingredient list and choose brands that do not contain artificial colors and flavorings. Always check the expiration date before buying.

*TIP: Once opened, use refrigerated egg substitute within a week.*

## GOOD TO KNOW

**Eggs are OK.** There's no need to avoid eggs because of concerns for cholesterol. Recent data shows that eggs are lower in cholesterol than previously thought (they actually have 185 mg of cholesterol, not the previously reported 210 mg).

**A woman's best friend.** Eggs are an outstanding source of choline, which may promote fetal brain development and help prevent birth defects. They also contribute iron to help nourish women who are at risk for iron-deficiency anemia.

**Eat on the cheap.** At about 25 cents each, eggs can make a delicious and filling snack that's easy on any budget.

## Whole Eggs

POWER-UP IDEAS

- Make a batch of hard-cooked eggs and keep in the refrigerator for a healthy breakfast or snack on the go.

- For a breakfast that works with the Simply Filling technique, enjoy poached eggs with a slice of toasted reduced-calorie bread.

- If you're short on time, buy hard-cooked eggs at your supermarket's salad bar or deli.

TAKE NOTE

- Eggs contain lutein, an antioxidant that may help prevent eye disease in older adults.

- Protein found in eggs is the highest quality protein found in any food.

- One hard-cooked or poached egg has a *PointsPlus* value of *2*.

## Egg Whites

POWER-UP IDEAS

- If health concerns limit you to 4 egg yolks a week, making an egg white omelet lets you enjoy eggs and follow doctor's orders.

- Add leftover cooked vegetables to omelets or frittatas to make filling, budget-minded meals.

- Make a scrambled egg white taco for a flavor-packed breakfast: Spray a nonstick skillet with cooking spray and cook diced onion and bell pepper until soft; add egg whites and cook until set. Spoon into a whole wheat flour tortilla and top with fat-free salsa.

TAKE NOTE

- To separate the whites from the yolks, use an egg separator or a funnel; passing the yolk back and forth from the shell halves can introduce bacteria. To keep the yolks, for every 4 egg yolks, stir in $1/8$ teaspoon salt or $1\frac{1}{2}$ teaspoons sugar and freeze for up to 6 months. The addition of the salt or sugar prevents the yolks from becoming too thick.

- Two egg whites contain about the same amount of protein as an ounce of meat, poultry, or seafood.

- Three egg whites have a *PointsPlus* value of *1*.

## Refrigerated Egg Substitute

POWER-UP IDEAS

- Use these convenient eggs to make a scramble or an omelet in a hurry—just pour and cook.

- Use egg substitute instead of whole eggs in recipes for cakes, muffins, and cookies.

- Refrigerated egg substitute is pasteurized, so it is safe to eat without cooking. Add it to smoothies for an instant protein boost.

TAKE NOTE

- $1/4$ cup of egg substitute is equivalent in volume to 1 egg.

- Refrigerated egg substitute is a convenient and easy way for vegetarians to get the protein they need.

- $1/4$ cup fat-free or regular egg substitute has a *PointsPlus* value of *1*.

## In this chapter

# Turkey Sausages with Scrambled Eggs and Peppers

SERVES 4

▲ 12 ounces ground skinless turkey breast

▲ ¼ cup finely chopped onion

4 tablespoons chopped fresh flat-leaf parsley

½ teaspoon fennel seeds

½ teaspoon dried sage

¼ teaspoon plus ⅛ teaspoon salt

¼ teaspoon black pepper

⅛ teaspoon red pepper flakes

▲ 2 red or yellow bell peppers, each cut into 8 slices

3 teaspoons olive oil

▲ 8 large egg whites

▲ 1 tablespoon fat-free milk

PER SERVING (2 sausages, ⅓ cup eggs, and about ½ cup bell pepper):
157 Cal, 5 g Total Fat, 1 g Sat Fat, 0 g Trans Fat, 25 mg Chol, 371 mg Sod, 6 g Carb, 4 g Sugar, 2 g Fib, 24 g Prot, 26 mg Calc.

**1** Spray broiler rack with nonstick spray and preheat broiler.

**2** Combine turkey, onion, 2 tablespoons of parsley, fennel seeds, sage, ¼ teaspoon of salt, ⅛ teaspoon of black pepper, and red pepper flakes in medium bowl. With damp hands, shape mixture into 8 (½-inch-thick) patties.

**3** Place patties and bell peppers on prepared broiler rack; drizzle evenly with 2 teaspoons of oil. Broil 4 inches from heat, turning patties once and peppers often, until patties are cooked through and peppers are tender, about 12 minutes.

**4** Meanwhile, whisk together egg whites, remaining 2 tablespoons parsley, milk, remaining ⅛ teaspoon salt, and ⅛ teaspoon black pepper in large bowl.

**5** Heat remaining 1 teaspoon oil in large nonstick skillet over medium heat. Add egg white mixture and cook, stirring frequently, just until set, 2–3 minutes. Serve with sausage and bell peppers.

**FYI** To ensure that the sausages are moist, take care not to overcook them. The patties should be golden in spots and firm in the center.

# Smoked Salmon Scramble with Potatoes and Creamy Dill Sauce

SERVES 4

▲ 1 pound red potatoes, cut into ³/₄-inch wedges

▲ ³/₄ cup plain fat-free yogurt

1 tablespoon chopped fresh dill

¹/₈ teaspoon salt

¹/₈ teaspoon black pepper

▲ 2 large eggs

▲ 4 large egg whites

1 tablespoon prepared horseradish, drained

3 teaspoons olive oil

▲ 1 cup halved cherry tomatoes

▲ 1 medium sweet onion, chopped

2 ounces sliced smoked salmon, cut into ¹/₂-inch pieces

PER SERVING (¹/₂ cup egg mixture, ³/₄ cup potatoes, 2 tablespoons tomatoes, and 2 tablespoons sauce): 227 Cal, 7 g Total Fat, 2 g Sat Fat, 0 g Trans Fat, 112 mg Chol, 329 mg Sod, 28 g Carb, 8 g Sugar, 3 g Fib, 15 g Prot, 132 mg Calc.

**1** Bring potatoes and enough cold water to cover to boil in medium saucepan. Reduce heat; partially cover and simmer until potatoes are fork-tender, about 8 minutes. Drain and keep warm.

**2** Meanwhile, stir together yogurt, dill, salt, and pepper in small bowl. Transfer 2 tablespoons of yogurt mixture to medium bowl. Add eggs and egg whites to medium bowl and whisk mixture until smooth. To make sauce, stir horseradish into yogurt mixture in small bowl.

**3** Heat 1 teaspoon of oil in medium nonstick skillet over medium heat. Add tomatoes and cook, stirring frequently, until just softened, 2–3 minutes. Cover and keep warm.

**4** Heat remaining 2 teaspoons oil in large nonstick skillet over medium heat. Add onion and cook, stirring frequently, until softened and lightly browned, about 5 minutes. Add salmon and cook, turning gently with tongs, until it begins to turn white, 2–3 minutes. Add egg mixture and cook, stirring frequently, just until set, 2–3 minutes. Divide egg mixture, potatoes, and tomatoes among 4 serving plates. Drizzle sauce evenly over potatoes.

**FYI** To help the smoked salmon cook evenly, separate the pieces with your fingers before adding them to the skillet in step 4.

# Potato Torta with Romesco Sauce

SERVES 4

▲ 12 ounces small red potatoes, thinly sliced

▲ ½ cup chopped roasted red bell peppers, drained (not oil packed)

▲ 1 small tomato, quartered

2 tablespoons slivered almonds

2 tablespoons orange juice

1 small garlic clove, chopped

½ teaspoon smoked paprika

¼ teaspoon ground cumin

▲ 1 cup fat-free egg substitute

1 tablespoon minced fresh chives

¼ teaspoon salt

⅛ teaspoon black pepper

1 tablespoon olive oil

PER SERVING (¼ of torta with ¼ cup sauce):
144 Cal, 6 g Total Fat, 1 g Sat Fat, 0 g Trans Fat, 0 mg Chol, 294 mg Sod, 17 g Carb, 2 g Sugar, 2 g Fib, 8 g Prot, 46 mg Calc.

**1** Bring potatoes and enough cold water to cover to boil in medium saucepan. Reduce heat; partially cover and simmer until potatoes are fork-tender, about 6 minutes. Drain.

**2** Meanwhile, to make sauce, combine roasted peppers, tomato, almonds, orange juice, garlic, paprika, and cumin in food processor and process until smooth. Set aside.

**3** Whisk together egg substitute, chives, salt, and black pepper in medium bowl.

**4** Heat oil in 12-inch nonstick skillet over medium heat. Add potatoes, spreading them in a single layer, and cook until lightly browned, about 5 minutes (do not stir). Turn potatoes, keeping them in single layer, and cook until lightly browned, 3–4 minutes.

**5** Pour egg mixture evenly over potatoes. Reduce heat and cook, covered, lifting edges with spatula once or twice, until eggs are set, 4–5 minutes. Cut into wedges and serve with sauce.

**FYI** For a smart accompaniment with this hearty egg dish, toss your favorite purchased bag of mixed baby salad greens with balsamic vinegar and salt and pepper to taste.

**POTATO TORTA WITH ROMESCO SAUCE**

**2 teaspoons olive oil**

▲ **2 poblano peppers, cut into ½-inch strips**

▲ **1 medium sweet onion, chopped**

▲ **1 cup fat-free egg substitute**

**2 tablespoons chopped fresh cilantro**

**¼ teaspoon ground cumin**

**¼ teaspoon salt**

**⅛ teaspoon black pepper**

**½ avocado, peeled, pitted, and diced**

**PER SERVING (¾ cup):**
119 Cal, 6 g Total Fat, 1 g Sat Fat,
0 g Trans Fat, 0 mg Chol,
247 mg Sod, 12 g Carb, 4 g Sugar,
4 g Fib, 7 g Prot, 45 mg Calc

# Egg, Poblano, and Avocado Scramble

**1** Heat oil in large nonstick skillet over medium-high heat. Add poblanos and onion; cook, stirring occasionally, until vegetables soften, 5 minutes.

**2** Meanwhile, whisk together egg substitute, cilantro, cumin, salt, and black pepper in medium bowl.

**3** Pour egg mixture evenly over poblano mixture. Reduce heat and cook, stirring frequently, just until eggs are set, about 3 minutes. Remove skillet from heat. Gently stir in avocado.

**FYI** These zesty eggs are delicious with a side of lean cooked ham. A 2-ounce slice per serving will increase the *PointsPlus* value by *2*.

# Broccolini and Goat Cheese Frittata

SERVES 4

▲ ½ bunch broccolini, cut into 1-inch pieces

▲ 1 cup fat-free egg substitute

1 tablespoon chopped fresh marjoram or flat-leaf parsley

¼ teaspoon salt

⅛ teaspoon black pepper

1 tablespoon olive oil

▲ ½ cup thinly sliced scallions

▲ 2 small plum tomatoes, thinly sliced

½ cup crumbled low-fat goat cheese

**PER SERVING** (¼ of frittata): 89 Cal, 5 g Total Fat, 1 g Sat Fat, 0 g Trans Fat, 0 mg Chol, 438 mg Sod, 5 g Carb, 2 g Sugar, 1 g Fib, 9 g Prot, 94 mg Calc.

**1** Put broccolini in steamer basket; set in saucepan over 1 inch of boiling water. Cover tightly and steam until crisp-tender, 5–7 minutes.

**2** Meanwhile, preheat broiler. Whisk together egg substitute, marjoram, salt, and pepper in medium bowl. Set aside.

**3** Heat oil in large ovenproof nonstick skillet over medium heat. Add scallions and cook, stirring frequently, until softened, about 2 minutes. Stir in broccolini. Pour egg mixture over vegetable mixture, stirring gently to combine. Cook until eggs are almost set, 3–4 minutes.

**4** Arrange tomato slices in single layer on top of frittata and sprinkle with cheese. Place frittata under broiler and broil 4 inches from heat until center is set and cheese is hot, about 3 minutes. Let stand 2 minutes before serving. Cut into wedges.

**FYI** A fresh fruit salad is perfect to round out this breakfast dish. To make one, stir together 2 cups fresh pineapple or cantaloupe chunks with 1 cup fresh blueberries and 1 tablespoon lime juice.

# Caramelized Onion and Zucchini Frittata

SERVES 4

1 tablespoon olive oil

▲ 1 large sweet onion, thinly sliced

2 ½ tablespoons thinly sliced fresh sage

1 ½ teaspoons brown sugar

▲ 1 medium zucchini, halved lengthwise and thinly sliced

▲ 2 large eggs

▲ 4 large egg whites

2 tablespoons chopped fresh flat-leaf parsley

▲ 1 tablespoon fat-free milk

¼ teaspoon salt

⅛ teaspoon black pepper

1 tablespoon grated Parmesan cheese

PER SERVING (¼ of frittata):
130 Cal, 6 g Total Fat, 1 g Sat Fat,
0 g Trans Fat, 109 mg Chol,
266 mg Sod, 11 g Carb, 7 g Sugar,
1 g Fib, 9 g Prot, 64 mg Calc.

**3** PointsPlus® value

**1** Heat oil in large nonstick skillet over medium heat. Add onion and cook, stirring occasionally, until softened, about 5 minutes. Add sage and brown sugar; reduce heat and cook, stirring occasionally, until onion is tender and lightly browned, 10–12 minutes. Stir in zucchini. Cook, covered, stirring occasionally, until zucchini is tender, about 8 minutes.

**2** Meanwhile, whisk together eggs, egg whites, parsley, milk, salt, and pepper in medium bowl.

**3** Pour egg mixture evenly over vegetables. Cook, covered, lifting edges with rubber spatula every 2 minutes, until eggs are set, 6–8 minutes. Sprinkle evenly with Parmesan. Let stand 2 minutes before serving. Cut into wedges.

**FYI** You can add some heat and bulk up on veggies by adding a thinly sliced poblano pepper along with the onion in step 1.

# Spinach-Garlic Grits with Poached Eggs

SERVES 4

2 ½ cups water

¼ teaspoon salt

▲ ½ cup quick-cooking grits

2 teaspoons olive oil

2 garlic cloves, minced

▲ 3 cups coarsely chopped fresh spinach

▲ ¾ cup fresh or frozen corn kernels, thawed

2 tablespoons fat-free cream cheese

¼ teaspoon sugar

⅛ teaspoon black pepper

2 teaspoons apple-cider vinegar

▲ 4 large eggs

PER SERVING (¾ cup grits with 1 egg):
208 Cal, 8 g Total Fat, 2 g Sat Fat,
0 g Trans Fat, 216 mg Chol,
291 mg Sod, 25 g Carb, 2 g Sugar,
2 g Fib, 11 g Prot, 79 mg Calc.

6 PointsPlus value

**1** Combine water and salt in large saucepan; bring to boil over medium-high heat. Slowly pour in grits in thin, steady stream, stirring constantly. Reduce heat and cook, covered, stirring often, until grits are softened and creamy, about 15 minutes.

**2** Meanwhile, heat oil in large nonstick skillet over medium heat. Add garlic and cook, stirring constantly, until fragrant, 30 seconds. Add spinach and corn and cook, stirring frequently, until spinach is wilted, 1–2 minutes.

**3** Add spinach mixture, cream cheese, sugar, and pepper to grits; stir until well blended. Cover and keep warm.

**4** Fill another large skillet half full with water and bring to boil over high heat. Add vinegar and reduce heat until water is simmering. Carefully break eggs into water. Simmer until whites are opaque and yolks are set, 5–6 minutes.

**5** Divide grits mixture evenly among 4 shallow serving bowls. Using slotted spoon, top each serving of grits with an egg and serve at once.

**FYI** You can get a jump start on this recipe by making the grits ahead. Prepare as directed through step 3 and transfer the grits to a microwavable container and let cool to room temperature. Cover and refrigerate overnight. To reheat, cover with wax paper and microwave on High 1–2 minutes.

# Blueberry Dutch Baby

SERVES 4

2 teaspoons butter

▲ 1 cup fat-free milk

3/4 cup all-purpose flour

▲ 1/2 cup egg substitute

1 tablespoon canola oil

1/8 teaspoon ground cinnamon

Pinch salt

▲ 3/4 cup fresh or frozen blueberries

2 teaspoons confectioners' sugar

▲ 1/2 cup plain fat-free Greek yogurt

**PER SERVING (1 wedge with
2 tablespoons yogurt):**
200 Cal, 6 g Total Fat, 2 g Sat Fat,
0 g Trans Fat, 6 mg Chol,
132 mg Sod, 27 g Carb, 8 g Sugar,
1 g Fib, 10 g Prot, 112 mg Calc.

**1** Preheat oven to 450°F. Place butter in 9-inch oven-proof skillet or glass pie plate. Place in oven and heat until butter melts, 2–3 minutes.

**2** Meanwhile, combine milk, flour, egg substitute, oil, cinnamon, and salt in blender and process until very smooth, about 1 minute.

**3** Remove skillet from oven and swirl so that butter covers bottom and side of skillet. Pour in milk mixture and sprinkle evenly with blueberries. Bake until pancake is puffed and lightly browned, 25–30 minutes. Dust with confectioners' sugar. Cut into wedges and serve with yogurt.

**FYI** This festive pancake is also delicious prepared with an equal amount of fresh or frozen raspberries or blackberries instead of the blueberries (or use a combination of berries).

# Walnut-Spice Matzo Soufflé with Strawberry Compote

SERVES 4

3 1/2 tablespoons plus 1/4 cup sugar

2 whole wheat matzos, broken into large pieces

1/3 cup walnuts

2 large egg yolks

2 tablespoons orange juice

▲ 5 large egg whites, at room temperature

1 teaspoon lemon juice

1/4 teaspoon salt

1/4 teaspoon cinnamon

▲ 2 cups sliced fresh strawberries

PER SERVING (about 1 1/4 cups soufflé with 1/2 cup compote): 248 Cal, 9 g Total Fat, 1 g Sat Fat, 0 g Trans Fat, 105 mg Chol, 219 mg Sod, 37 g Carb, 22 g Sugar, 4 g Fib, 10 g Prot, 42 mg Calc.

**1** Preheat oven to 400°F. Spray 8-inch square baking dish with nonstick spray. Dust bottom and sides of dish with 1 tablespoon of sugar.

**2** Place matzos in large bowl of cold water. Let stand until softened, about 8 minutes. Remove matzos and squeeze dry; discard water. Return matzos to bowl.

**3** Combine walnuts and 1 tablespoon of remaining sugar in food processor and process until finely ground. Add walnut mixture, egg yolks, and orange juice to matzos and whisk until well blended.

**4** With electric mixer on high speed, beat egg whites, lemon juice, and salt in large bowl until foamy. Add 1/4 cup of remaining sugar, 1 tablespoon at a time, beating until stiff, glossy peaks form. Gently whisk one quarter of egg white mixture into matzo mixture just until blended. Gently fold in remaining egg white mixture with a rubber spatula just until no streaks of white remain. Spoon batter into baking dish; spread evenly.

**5** Stir together 1/2 tablespoon of remaining sugar and cinnamon in small dish; sprinkle evenly over soufflé. Bake until toothpick inserted into center comes out clean, 18–20 minutes. Transfer to rack to cool slightly.

**6** Meanwhile, combine strawberries and remaining 1 tablespoon sugar in medium bowl. Let stand, stirring occasionally, 10 minutes. Serve with warm soufflé.

**WALNUT-SPICE MATZO SOUFFLÉ
WITH STRAWBERRY COMPOTE**

# Overnight Ricotta and Swiss Chard Strata

SERVES 6

2 tablespoons olive oil

▲ 1 (8-ounce) package cremini mushrooms, sliced

▲ 4 scallions, thinly sliced

2 garlic cloves, minced

1 teaspoon dried thyme

▲ ¼ cup reduced-sodium vegetable broth

▲ ½ pound Swiss chard, stems thinly sliced and leaves chopped

½ teaspoon salt

¼ teaspoon black pepper

4 slices multigrain bread, toasted and cubed (3 cups)

▲ 3 large eggs

▲ 4 large egg whites

▲ 1 cup fat-free milk

⅔ cup part-skim ricotta cheese

**PER SERVING (about 1 cup):**
222 Cal, 11 g Total Fat, 3 g Sat Fat, 0 g Trans Fat, 117 mg Chol, 505 mg Sod, 18 g Carb, 5 g Sugar, 3 g Fib, 14 g Prot, 190 mg Calc.

**1** Spray shallow 2-quart baking dish with nonstick spray.

**2** Heat oil in large nonstick skillet over medium heat. Add mushrooms and cook, stirring frequently, until tender and lightly browned, about 6 minutes. Add scallions, garlic, and thyme; cook, stirring frequently, until scallions are softened, about 2 minutes. Add broth and bring to boil. Add chard in batches, and cook, stirring frequently, until chard wilts, about 2 minutes. Reduce heat and cook, covered, stirring occasionally, until chard is tender, 8–10 minutes. Stir in ¼ teaspoon of salt and ⅛ teaspoon of pepper. Spread vegetables in baking dish; sprinkle bread cubes evenly over vegetables.

**3** Whisk together eggs, egg whites, milk, ricotta, remaining ¼ teaspoon salt, and remaining ⅛ teaspoon pepper in large bowl. Pour egg mixture evenly over bread cubes and vegetables, pressing bread cubes into egg mixture to moisten. Cover with foil and refrigerate at least 8 hours or overnight.

**4** Preheat oven to 350°F.

**5** Uncover strata and bake until lightly browned and knife inserted into center comes out clean, 20–25 minutes. Let stand 5 minutes before serving. Cut into wedges.

# Crustless Leek and Feta Quiche

**SERVES 6**

▲ ½ cup Wehani brown rice or short-grain brown rice

2 teaspoons olive oil

▲ 2 leeks, cleaned and thinly sliced (white and light green parts only)

¼ cup chopped fresh flat-leaf parsley

2 tablespoons chopped fresh dill

▲ 4 large eggs

▲ 2 large egg whites

▲ ¾ cup fat-free milk

¼ teaspoon salt

⅛ teaspoon black pepper

¾ cup crumbled low-fat feta cheese

**PER SERVING (1 wedge):**
191 Cal, 7 g Total Fat, 3 g Sat Fat, 0 g Trans Fat, 149 mg Chol, 414 mg Sod, 20 g Carb, 3 g Sugar, 2 g Fib, 12 g Prot, 131 mg Calc.

**5 PointsPlus® value**

**1** Cook rice according to package directions.

**2** Meanwhile, preheat oven to 350°F. Spray 9-inch deep-dish pie plate with nonstick spray.

**3** Heat oil in large nonstick skillet over medium heat. Add leeks and cook, stirring frequently, until softened, 7–9 minutes. Stir in parsley and dill; set aside. Whisk together eggs, egg whites, milk, salt, and pepper in medium bowl.

**4** Fluff rice with fork. Transfer to pie plate and spread evenly. Sprinkle leeks over top. Pour egg mixture evenly over leeks and rice; sprinkle with feta. Bake until knife inserted into center comes out clean, 30–35 minutes. Let stand 5 minutes before serving. Cut into 6 wedges.

**FYI** Wehani rice is an aromatic copper-colored brown rice with a nutty flavor and a large grain. Distinctive and delicious, it's found in the natural foods sections of most supermarkets.

WHOLE WHEAT BISCUIT
AND EGG SANDWICHES

# Whole Wheat Biscuit and Egg Sandwiches

SERVES 6

1 cup whole wheat pastry flour

1/2 cup all-purpose flour

2 teaspoons baking powder

1/2 teaspoon baking soda

1/8 teaspoon salt

▲ 1/2 cup plain fat-free yogurt

▲ 2 tablespoons fat-free milk

2 tablespoons canola oil

▲ 6 large eggs

1/4 teaspoon coarsely ground black pepper

▲ 1 large tomato, cut into 6 (1/4-inch-thick) slices

Chopped fresh flat-leaf parsley, for garnish (optional)

**PER SERVING** (1 filled biscuit):
247 Cal, 10 g Total Fat, 2 g Sat Fat,
0 g Trans Fat, 216 mg Chol,
421 mg Sod, 28 g Carb, 3 g Sugar,
3 g Fib, 11 g Prot, 118 mg Calc.

**1** Preheat oven to 425°F. Spray large baking sheet with nonstick spray.

**2** Whisk together pastry flour, all-purpose flour, baking powder, baking soda, and salt in medium bowl. Whisk together yogurt, milk, and oil in small bowl. Add yogurt mixture to flour mixture, stirring just until soft dough forms.

**3** Turn dough onto lightly floured work surface. Knead about 6 times or until dough just holds together. With lightly floured hands, pat dough into 7 1/2-x-5-inch rectangle. With lightly floured knife, cut dough in half lengthwise, then crosswise in thirds, to make total of 6 (2 1/2-inch) biscuits. Transfer biscuits to baking sheet and bake until lightly browned on bottoms, 10–12 minutes. Transfer biscuits to rack and let cool slightly, about 5 minutes.

**4** Meanwhile, spray 12-inch nonstick skillet with nonstick spray and set over medium heat. Crack eggs into skillet; cover and cook until yolks just begin to set, 3–5 minutes. Sprinkle with pepper.

**5** Cut biscuits in half horizontally and fill each with 1 egg and 1 tomato slice. Sprinkle with parsley if using.

**FYI** Love cheese? For another *1 PointsPlus* value per serving, assemble the biscuits as directed in step 5 and top each egg with a 1-ounce slice fat-free American cheese before adding the tomato. Serve the sandwiches with grape clusters.

▲ **1 cup canned reduced-sodium black beans, rinsed and drained**

▲ **⅓ cup fat-free salsa**

½ small avocado, peeled and pitted

Juice of ½ lime

▲ **1 cup fat-free egg substitute**

¼ teaspoon chili powder

4 (8-inch) multigrain tortillas, warmed

**PER SERVING (1 filled tortilla):**
156 Cal, 5 g Total Fat, 0 g Sat Fat,
0g Trans Fat, 0 mg Chol,
568 mg Sod, 25 g Carb, 1 g Sugar,
13 g Fib, 14 g Prot, 43 mg Calc.

# Egg and Avocado Wraps

**1** Combine beans and salsa in small skillet. Cook over medium heat, stirring frequently and partially mashing beans with wooden spoon, until mixture is heated through, about 5 minutes.

**2** Meanwhile, combine avocado and lime juice in small bowl and mash with fork until smooth.

**3** Whisk together egg substitute and chili powder in medium bowl.

**4** Spray medium nonstick skillet with nonstick spray and set over medium-low heat. Add egg substitute and cook, stirring frequently, until set, 2–3 minutes.

**5** Spread each tortilla with 1 tablespoon of avocado mixture; top with ¼ cup of eggs and ¼ cup of bean mixture. Roll up and serve at once.

**FYI** For a hearty winter breakfast, you can serve each wrap with ½ cup fresh grapefruit sections topped with 1 tablespoon pomegranate seeds.

# Baby Greens Salad with Eggs and Walnuts

SERVES 4

UNDER 20 MINUTES

▲ 4 large eggs
1 tablespoon olive oil
1 tablespoon apple juice
2 teaspoons apple-cider vinegar
½ teaspoon whole-grain mustard
¼ teaspoon salt
⅛ teaspoon black pepper
▲ 1 (5-ounce) container mixed baby salad greens
▲ 4 radishes, sliced
▲ 2 tablespoons minced red onion
¼ cup walnuts, toasted and chopped

**PER SERVING (1 plate):**
160 Cal, 13 g Total Fat, 2 g Sat Fat,
0 g Trans Fat, 215 mg Chol,
233 mg Sod, 5 g Carb, 2 g Sugar,
2 g Fib, 8 g Prot, 30 mg Calc.

**1** Combine eggs and enough cold water to cover by 1 inch in medium saucepan; bring to boil over high heat. Remove saucepan from heat, cover, and let stand until eggs are hard cooked, 12 minutes. Rinse briefly under cold running water. When cool enough to handle, peel eggs. Cut each egg into quarters.

**2** Meanwhile, to make dressing, whisk together oil, apple juice, vinegar, mustard, salt, and pepper in large bowl.

**3** Add salad greens, radishes, and onion to dressing and toss to coat. Divide salad among 4 plates. Arrange eggs evenly on plates and sprinkle evenly with walnuts.

**FYI** To toast the walnuts, place them in a small dry skillet over medium-low heat. Toast, shaking the pan and stirring constantly, until lightly browned and fragrant, 3–4 minutes. Watch them carefully, as they can burn quickly. Transfer to a plate to cool.

# Tomatoes Stuffed with Tabbouleh Egg Salad

SERVES 4

1 cup water

▲ ⅓ cup bulgur

▲ 4 large hard-cooked eggs, peeled and chopped

½ cup chopped fresh flat-leaf parsley

▲ ½ red bell pepper, chopped

▲ 2 tablespoons chopped red onion

1 tablespoon lemon juice

1 tablespoon olive oil

¼ teaspoon salt

⅛ teaspoon black pepper

▲ 4 large tomatoes

**PER SERVING (1 stuffed tomato):**
191 Cal, 9 g Total Fat, 2 g Sat Fat,
0 g Trans Fat, 212 mg Chol,
226 mg Sod, 19 g Carb, 6 g Sugar,
5 g Fib, 10 g Prot, 62 mg Calc.

**1** Bring water to boil in medium saucepan. Stir in bulgur; remove pan from heat. Cover and let stand 25 minutes. Drain bulgur in colander, pressing out excess liquid with back of spoon.

**2** Transfer bulgur to large bowl. Stir in eggs, parsley, bell pepper, onion, lemon juice, oil, salt, and pepper.

**3** Slice off top fourth of each tomato; set aside. Remove and discard seeds from bottoms of tomatoes. With grapefruit spoon or small knife, scoop pulp from bottoms of tomatoes, leaving a ¼-inch-thick shell. Chop pulp and stir into bulgur mixture. Spoon evenly into tomato shells. Replace tops of tomatoes.

**FYI** To save on prep time, buy hard-cooked eggs from your supermarket salad bar.

**STUFFED TOMATOES WITH
TABBOULEH EGG SALAD**

# Milk Yogurt and Cheese

Breakfasts,
Brunches, and
Snacks

# Milk, Yogurt, and Cheese

## YOU NEED

2 servings per day; 3 if you're a teenager, a nursing mom, over 50, or if you weigh more than 250 pounds. A serving is 1 cup of fat-free milk or fat-free soy milk, 1 cup plain fat-free yogurt or artificially-sweetened flavored yogurt, 2 cups fat-free cottage cheese, $\frac{1}{2}$ cup fat-free ricotta cheese, or $1\frac{1}{2}$ ounces fat-free semi-soft or hard cheese.

## WHY THEY'RE ESSENTIAL

**Bone up on dairy.** Dairy products are an excellent source of calcium, which can help to reduce the risk of osteoporosis and fractures.

**Tune up your ticker.** Consuming milk and dairy foods can help you reduce your risk of cardiovascular disease and lower blood pressure.

**D does it all.** Vitamin D helps the body absorb calcium and plays an important role in bone health. Recent research has linked vitamin D deficiency to everything from decreasing the risk of asthma to diabetes, but more research is needed to confirm findings in relation to these conditions. Almost all the fluid milk sold in the U.S. is fortified with vitamin D, but other products made with milk, such as cheese and yogurt, are generally not fortified.

## WHAT TO BUY

**Milk:** Fat-free milk or fat-free soy milk.

*TIP: If you use soy milk, check the label to make sure it's sugar-free and calcium-fortified.*

**Yogurt:** Plain fat-free yogurt or artificially sweetened flavored yogurt.

*TIP: Fat-free Greek yogurt is thicker and tastes richer than regular yogurt and the PointsPlus value is the same.*

**Cheese:** Fat-free soft, semisoft, or hard cheeses.

*TIP: Choose cheeses with lots of flavor, such as fat-free feta or sharp Cheddar, which means you can use less.*

## GOOD TO KNOW

**Help for the lactose-intolerant.** Most supermarkets stock calcium-fortified lactose-free milk and yogurt. Look for calcium-fortified juices and cereals and don't forget about nondairy calcium sources such as canned salmon and sardines (eat the soft bones to get the calcium), leafy greens, and dried beans.

**Crack a smile.** The casein in milk prevents cavity-causing bacteria from sticking to teeth and enamel erosion.

## Fat-free milk

POWER-UP IDEAS

- Treat yourself to a cappuccino made with fat-free milk.
- Use fat-free milk instead of water to make oatmeal.
- Use fat-free milk for reconstituting canned soups such as cream of mushroom, cream of celery, or tomato.

TAKE NOTE

- Milk proteins can help muscles rebuild after strenuous exercise.
- Minerals in milk can prevent muscle cramps.
- Lactalabumin, a protein in milk, may help improve sleep quality and make you feel more alert the next morning.

## Plain fat-free yogurt

POWER-UP IDEAS

- Make a smoothie with plain fat-free yogurt and fresh fruit.
- Have plain fat-free yogurt for an afternoon snack.
- Make a dip for vegetables using plain fat-free yogurt instead of sour cream.

TAKE NOTE

- Because natural cultures in yogurt help with digestion, some people with lactose intolerance can enjoy yogurt.
- Check the label to be sure the yogurt contains active cultures; these help maintain the body's balance of good bacteria.
- A half cup of plain fat-free yogurt has about the same amount of protein as one egg.

## Fat-free cheeses

POWER-UP IDEAS

- Sprinkle shredded fat-free Cheddar cheese on a hot baked potato.
- Have fat-free cottage cheese and fresh fruit for a healthy and delicious snack.
- Spread fat-free ricotta cheese on whole wheat toast for a protein-rich breakfast.

TAKE NOTE

- If you're following heart-healthy recommendations to cut saturated fat, fat-free cheeses are a delicious option.
- Everyone loves cheese, so if you don't like milk, enjoy cheese to get the dairy-food nutrients you need.
- Semisoft fat-free cheese such as mozzarella or Cheddar can become tough if overheated; add them to hot foods and let the heat of the food soften the cheese.

## In this chapter

▲ 1¹⁄₂ cups fat-free milk

Pinch salt

▲ ¹⁄₄ cup quick-cooking barley

▲ ¹⁄₄ cup bulgur

▲ ¹⁄₄ cup old-fashioned rolled oats

¹⁄₄ cup raisins

¹⁄₄ cup sliced dried apricots

Pinch ground cinnamon

2 teaspoons maple syrup

2 tablespoons chopped pistachios

**PER SERVING** (¹⁄₂ cup):
207 Cal, 2 g Total Fat, 0 g Sat Fat,
0 g Trans Fat, 0 mg Chol,
81 mg Sod, 40 g Carb, 18 g Sugar,
6 g Fib, 7 g Prot, 134 mg Calc.

# Whole Grain Breakfast Porridge

**1** Put milk and salt in small saucepan and bring just to boil. Stir in barley, bulgur, oats, raisins, apricots, and cinnamon. Reduce heat and simmer, stirring frequently, until milk is absorbed and grains are tender, but still chewy, about 10 minutes.

**2** Remove from heat and stir in maple syrup. Spoon porridge into 4 serving bowls; sprinkle with pistachios and serve at once.

**FYI** For a complete breakfast, you can serve the porridge with fresh blueberries or sliced strawberries.

# Creamy Coffee-Banana Cooler

SERVES 2

UNDER 20 MINUTES

- ▲ 1 cup fat-free milk
- 1 cup chilled brewed espresso or coffee
- ▲ 1 ripe banana, sliced
- 1 teaspoon vanilla extract
- 1/8 teaspoon ground cinnamon
- Ice cubes

**PER SERVING (1 1/3 cups):**
102 Cal, 0 g Total Fat, 0 g Sat Fat,
0 g Trans Fat, 2 mg Chol,
55 mg Sod, 20 g Carb, 14 g Sugar,
2 g Fib, 5 g Prot, 160 mg Calc

Combine all ingredients except ice cubes in blender and blend at high speed until smooth and frothy. Serve in tall glasses over ice cubes.

**FYI** Enjoy this refreshing drink with an orange or tangerine for breakfast or as an afternoon pick-me-up that's packed with goodness.

# Fruit Muesli with Honeyed Yogurt

SERVES 4

▲ 1 cup old-fashioned rolled oats

▲ ½ cup fat-free milk

¼ cup chopped dried apricots

2 tablespoons golden raisins

2 tablespoons orange juice

▲ ½ cup plain fat-free yogurt

1 teaspoon honey

1 tablespoon chopped walnuts

**PER SERVING** (generous ¼ cup muesli and ¼ cup yogurt): 159 Cal, 3 g Total Fat, 1 g Sat Fat, 0 g Trans Fat, 1 mg Chol, 39 mg Sod, 29 g Carb, 14 g Sugar, 3 g Fib, 6 g Prot, 109 mg Calc.

**1**  Stir together oats, milk, apricots, raisins, and orange juice in medium bowl; let stand 30 minutes, stirring occasionally.

**2**  Meanwhile, stir together yogurt and honey in small bowl.

**3**  Divide oat mixture evenly among 4 cereal bowls. Top evenly with yogurt mixture and walnuts.

**FYI**  Traditionally muesli is served with chopped fresh apple and soaked from 1 to 30 minutes, depending on the texture you prefer.

**MAPLE-LEMON FRUIT
PARFAITS WITH YOGURT**

▲ **2 cups cubed pineapple**

▲ **2 kiwifruit, peeled and cubed**

▲ **1 large mango, peeled,
pitted, and cubed**

**1 teaspoon grated lemon zest**

**1 tablespoon lemon juice**

**1 teaspoon maple syrup**

▲ **2 cups plain fat-free yogurt**

**4 tablespoons low-fat granola**

**PER SERVING** (1 parfait):
189 Cal, 1 g Total Fat, 0 g Sat Fat,
0 g Trans Fat, 2 mg Chol,
105 mg Sod, 39 g Carb, 23 g Sugar,
3 g Fib, 8 g Prot, 270 mg Calc.

# Maple-Lemon Fruit Parfaits with Yogurt

**1** Stir together pineapple, kiwifruit, mango, lemon zest, lemon juice, and maple syrup in medium bowl.

**2** Spoon ¼ cup of yogurt into each of 4 parfait glasses; top each with ½ cup of pineapple mixture. Repeat layering once. Sprinkle parfaits evenly with granola and serve at once.

**FYI** Maple and lemon accentuate the flavor of any fruits, so you can use whatever fruit is in season to make these parfaits. Apples or pears would add crunch, berries color and flavor, and papaya would lend a tropical touch.

# Cheddar and Vegetable Frittata

SERVES 4

▲ 1 medium red or yellow bell pepper, sliced

▲ 3 large eggs

▲ 3 large egg whites

▲ 1 cup fat-free milk

¼ teaspoon salt

⅛ teaspoon black pepper

▲ 1 large tomato, chopped

▲ 1 cup shredded fat-free Cheddar cheese

2 tablespoons chopped fresh flat-leaf parsley

**PER SERVING (¼ of frittata):**
153 Cal, 4 g Total Fat, 1 g Sat Fat,
0 g Trans Fat, 167 mg Chol,
465 mg Sod, 11 g Carb, 6 g Sugar,
1 g Fib, 19 g Prot, 356 mg Calc.

1  Spray 10-inch ovenproof nonstick skillet with nonstick spray and set over medium heat. Add bell pepper and cook, stirring occasionally, until softened, 5 minutes. Transfer to small bowl.

2  Preheat broiler.

3  Whisk together eggs, egg whites, milk, salt, and pepper in large bowl. Stir in bell pepper, tomato, cheese, and parsley.

4  Wipe out skillet; spray with nonstick spray and set over medium heat. Add egg mixture, reduce heat to medium-low and cook until eggs are set, 8–10 minutes.

5  Place skillet under broiler and broil 5 inches from heat until frittata is set in center, 5 minutes. Cut into 4 wedges and serve at once.

**FYI**  To get more vegetables, cook a medium thinly sliced red onion with the bell pepper in step 1. Serve the frittata with cherry tomatoes and mixed greens tossed with balsamic vinegar, salt, and pepper to taste.

**CHEDDAR AND
VEGETABLE FRITTATA**

# Mozzarella, Roasted Pepper, and Basil Omelette

SERVES 2

UNDER 20 MINUTES

▲ **2 large eggs**

▲ **2 large egg whites**

▲ **1 tablespoon fat-free milk**

**¼ teaspoon black pepper**

**⅛ teaspoon salt**

**1 teaspoon olive oil**

▲ **⅓ cup shredded fat-free mozzarella cheese**

▲ **¼ cup chopped roasted red bell peppers (not oil packed)**

**1 tablespoon chopped fresh basil**

**PER SERVING (½ omelette):**
175 Cal, 11 g Total Fat, 4 g Sat Fat,
0 g Trans Fat, 225 mg Chol,
316 mg Sod, 4 g Carb, 2 g Sugar,
0 g Fib, 15 g Prot, 176 mg Calc

**1**  Beat eggs, egg whites, milk, pepper, and salt in medium bowl until frothy.

**2**  Heat oil in medium nonstick skillet over medium heat. Pour in egg mixture and cook, stirring gently with heatproof rubber spatula, until underside is set, about 2 minutes.

**3**  Sprinkle cheese, peppers, and basil evenly over half of omelette; with spatula, fold other half of omelette over filling and continue to cook until filling is heated through and eggs are set, about 1 minute longer.

**4**  Cut omelette in half and slide each half onto a plate.

**FYI**  You can fill the omelette with a small chopped plum tomato along with the cheese, peppers, and basil.

# Cottage Cheese and Salsa Pita Sandwiches

SERVES 4

UNDER 20 MINUTES

▲ 1 cup fat-free cottage cheese

▲ ¼ cup diced cucumber

▲ ¼ cup fat-free salsa

2 tablespoons chopped fresh cilantro

⅛ teaspoon ground cumin

2 (6-inch) whole wheat pita breads, warmed

▲ 4 Bibb lettuce leaves

**PER SERVING** (½ stuffed pita):
132 Cal, 1 g Total Fat, 0 g Sat Fat,
0 g Trans Fat, 3 mg Chol,
443 mg Sod, 23 g Carb, 3 g Sugar,
3 g Fib, 10 g Prot, 39 mg Calc.

1  Stir together cottage cheese, cucumber, salsa, cilantro, and cumin in small bowl.

2  Cut pitas in half. Divide lettuce and cottage cheese mixture among pita breads and serve at once.

**FYI**  These sandwiches make a great take-along lunch. Pack the cottage cheese mixture, pita bread, and lettuce separately and assemble just before eating.

**2 (6-inch) whole wheat pita breads**

▲ **1 English (seedless) cucumber, diced**

▲ **1 cup plain fat-free Greek yogurt**

**2 tablespoons chopped fresh dill**

**1 teaspoon ground cumin**

**1/2 teaspoon salt**

**1/8 teaspoon cayenne**

**PER SERVING (1/4 cup dip with 8 pita triangles):**
127 Cal, 1 g Total Fat, 0 g Sat Fat, 0 g Trans Fat, 0 mg Chol, 483 mg Sod, 22 g Carb, 3 g Sugar, 3 g Fib, 9 g Prot, 63 mg Calc.

# Cucumber-Yogurt Dip with Pita Chips

**1**  Preheat oven to 400°F.

**2**  To make chips, split each pita into 2 rounds; lightly coat both sides of each round with nonstick spray. Cut each round into 8 wedges; arrange wedges in single layer on large baking sheet. Bake until crisp and lightly toasted, 6–7 minutes. Transfer to rack to cool.

**3**  To make dip, stir together remaining ingredients in medium bowl. Serve dip with pita chips.

**FYI  Make a double batch of this dip and use it for dipping fresh vegetables or as a mayonnaise substitute on sandwiches. The dip can be refrigerated up to 4 days.**

# Creamy Sun-Dried Tomato Dip

SERVES 8

▲ 1 (16-ounce) container fat-free cottage cheese

¼ cup fat-free mayonnaise

¼ cup dry-packed sun-dried tomatoes, chopped (not oil packed)

▲ 2 scallions, chopped

2 teaspoons lemon juice

¼ teaspoon hot pepper sauce

2 tablespoons chopped fresh basil

▲ 8 cups assorted cut-up vegetables

**PER SERVING** (¼ cup dip and ½ cup vegetables):
76 Cal, 0 g Total Fat, 0 g Sat Fat, 0 g Trans Fat, 3 mg Chol, 322 mg Sod, 12 g Carb, 7 g Sugar, 2 g Fib, 8 g Prot, 56 mg Calc.

Combine cottage cheese, mayonnaise, tomatoes, scallions, lemon juice, and pepper sauce in food processor and process until smooth. Transfer to medium bowl and stir in basil. Cover and refrigerate until well chilled, at least 2 hours or up to 2 days. Serve with vegetables.

**FYI** Always keep cut-up vegetables and a healthful dip such as this one in the refrigerator. When you or your family need a snack, you're more likely to make a healthy choice if the prep is already done.

# Cheese and Black Bean Nachos

36 baked low-fat tortilla chips

▲ 1 cup shredded fat-free
Monterey Jack cheese

▲ 1 (15-ounce) can black beans,
rinsed and drained

▲ 2 plum tomatoes, chopped

▲ 2 scallions, thinly sliced

▲ 1 jalapeño pepper, seeded
and minced

3 tablespoons chopped
fresh cilantro

Lime wedges

**PER SERVING** (¼ of dish):
222 Cal, 1 g Total Fat, 0 g Sat Fat,
0 g Trans Fat, 3 mg Chol,
434 mg Sod, 36 g Carb, 5 g Sugar,
6 g Fib, 16 g Prot, 476 mg Calc.

**1** Preheat oven to 400°F. Spray large baking sheet with nonstick spray.

**2** Arrange tortilla chips in single layer on baking sheet. Sprinkle evenly with cheese. Top with beans, tomatoes, scallions, and jalapeño.

**3** Bake until heated through and cheese is melted and bubbling, about 20 minutes. Sprinkle with cilantro. Serve with lime wedges.

**FYI** To make the nachos more healthful and filling, add a chopped red or green bell pepper along with the beans in step 2.

CHEESE AND BLACK
BEAN NACHOS

# Lean Meats

Beef, Pork, and Lamb
Main Dishes

# Lean Meats: Beef, Pork, and Lamb

### YOU NEED

1 to 2 servings per day of lean protein; 2 to 3 ounces of cooked beef, pork, or lamb count as 1 serving.

### WHY THEY'RE ESSENTIAL

**Satisfy your hunger.** Protein takes longer to digest than carbohydrates, so a small portion with each meal can help you feel full longer.

**Get a fundamental mineral.** Meats provide the most easily absorbed source of iron in the diet, which is required to transport oxygen to every tissue of the body.

**Meats have everything from B to Zinc.** B vitamins, which provide a range of functions, from helping to maintain a healthy nervous system to healthy skin and good vision, are all plentiful in meats. They're also an excellent source of zinc, which helps sustain the immune system and plays a factor in cognitive function.

**Meat is a complete protein.** Meats contain some of each one of the essential amino acids your body needs to build and repair body tissues.

### WHAT TO BUY

**Beef:** Rump roast, tenderloin, cube steak, flank steak, filet mignon, sirloin, round steak, and lean ground beef with 7% fat or less.
*TIP: Trim any visible fat from roasts or steaks before cooking.*

**Pork:** Center loin, tenderloin, sirloin, top loin, pork chops, and lean ham.
*TIP: Avoid buying pre-marinated pork tenderloin—it can be very high in sodium.*

**Lamb:** Lamb chops.
*TIP: If you shop in a supermarket with an on-site butcher, have him trim the meat away from the bone of the chops to create elegant Frenched lamb chops.*

### GOOD TO KNOW

**Enough already.** Women need about 46 grams of protein a day, and men about 56 grams. If you're eating a diet with a variety of healthy foods, you're most likely getting enough protein. A 3-ounce serving of meat gives you about 21 grams and a cup of yogurt has about 11 grams. Don't forget: Foods like grains and pasta have small amounts of protein that add to your total.

**Be wise about size.** A 3-ounce cooked portion of beef, pork, or lamb is about the size of a deck of cards.

# Beef

## POWER-UP IDEAS

- Build a better burger with a whole wheat bun, extra tomato slices, a raw onion slice, and dark leafy lettuce.
- Stretch a steak by serving it thinly sliced and paired with a whole grain side dish, fresh vegetables, and a salad.
- Skip the gravy when you make a roast and serve it with vegetables that you can roast at the same time.

## TAKE NOTE

- Selenium, a trace mineral found in beef and other animal protein, works as an antioxidant to reduce risk of heart disease.
- Lean trimmed beef is also a source of monounsaturated fat, the same good-for-your heart fat found in olive oil and salmon.
- A 3-ounce portion of beef contains as much iron as nearly 3 cups of fresh spinach.

# Pork

## POWER-UP IDEAS

- Make chilis and stews with cubes of pork tenderloin instead of beef for a change of taste.
- Cut pork chops into thin strips to use in a stir-fry.
- Keep lean ham on hand and enjoy 1 ounce with a small apple for an afternoon snack.

## TAKE NOTE

- Pork is an excellent source of the vitamin thiamine, which is essential to metabolize other nutrients such as protein and carbohydrate.
- Pork tenderloin contains about the same amount of fat as skinless chicken breast.
- Lean pork can be dry if over-cooked; be sure to cook it just to an internal temperature of 145°F.

# Lamb

## POWER-UP IDEAS

- Lamb chops are as quick and easy to prepare as steak or pork chops and they make any weeknight meal special.
- To season lamb chops, use the spice blend you keep on hand for steaks, or simply sprinkle them with salt and pepper to bring out the flavor.
- Marinate lamb and other lean meats to tenderize and add flavor before cooking.

## TAKE NOTE

- Lamb, like other meats, is an excellent source of iron, B vitamins, zinc, and selenium.
- American lamb is a better environmental choice for Americans than New Zealand lamb because it's produced closer to home.
- Cook lamb to the same temperature that you cook roast beef or steak; 145°F will be medium.

# Grilled Sirloin and Arugula Salad with Balsamic Vinaigrette

SERVES 4

UNDER 20 MINUTES

1 small shallot, minced

1 garlic clove, minced

¼ teaspoon salt

½ teaspoon black pepper

▲ 1 pound boneless sirloin steak, about ½ inch thick, trimmed

1 tablespoon olive oil

1 tablespoon balsamic vinegar

▲ 8 cups lightly packed arugula

PER SERVING (3 slices steak with 2 cups arugula):
209 Cal, 9 g Total Fat, 2 g Sat Fat, 0 g Trans Fat, 49 mg Chol, 358 mg Sod, 4 g Carb, 2 g Sugar, 1 g Fib, 27 g Prot, 89 mg Calc.

**1**  Stir together shallot, garlic, ¼ teaspoon of salt, and ¼ teaspoon of pepper in small bowl. Rub mixture onto all sides of steak; let stand at room temperature 10 minutes.

**2**  Spray large ridged grill pan with nonstick spray and set over medium-high heat. Add steak and cook until instant-read thermometer inserted into center of steak registers 145°F for medium, 3–4 minutes on each side. Transfer to cutting board and let stand 5 minutes.

**3**  Meanwhile, whisk together oil, vinegar, and remaining ¼ teaspoon salt and ¼ teaspoon pepper in large bowl. Add arugula and toss to coat.

**4**  Cut steak across grain into 12 slices. Divide steak among 4 serving plates; top evenly with arugula mixture and serve at once.

**FYI**  To make an easy side dish, you can microwave a 12-ounce package of steam-in-the bag green beans according to the package directions. Toss with lemon juice and salt and pepper to taste.

# Grilled Korean Steak in Lettuce Cups

SERVES 4

UNDER 20 MINUTES

▲ **6 scallions**

**3 tablespoons reduced-sodium soy sauce**

**2 teaspoons Asian (dark) sesame oil**

**1 teaspoon packed brown sugar**

**$\frac{1}{2}$ teaspoon black pepper**

▲ **1 pound boneless sirloin steak, about $\frac{1}{2}$ inch thick, trimmed**

▲ **2 red bell peppers, very thinly sliced**

▲ **8 radishes, thinly sliced**

▲ **1 carrot, coarsely shredded**

▲ **16 large Bibb lettuce leaves**

**PER SERVING (4 filled lettuce cups):**
229 Cal, 8 g Total Fat, 2 g Sat Fat,
0 g Trans Fat, 49 mg Chol,
478 mg Sod, 11 g Carb, 6 g Sugar,
3 g Fib, 29 g Prot, 70 mg Calc.

**1** Mince 2 scallions. Combine minced scallions, soy sauce, sesame oil, brown sugar, and black pepper in zip-close plastic bag; add steak. Squeeze out air and seal bag; turn to coat steak. Let stand at room temperature 5 minutes.

**2** Spray large ridged grill pan with nonstick spray and set over medium-high heat. Add steak and cook until instant-read thermometer inserted into center of steak registers 145°F for medium, 3–4 minutes on each side. Transfer to cutting board and let stand 5 minutes. Cut across grain into 16 slices.

**3** Meanwhile, cut remaining 4 scallions into 1-inch pieces. Divide scallions, bell peppers, radishes, and carrot evenly among lettuce leaves; top lettuce leaves evenly with steak. Serve at once.

**FYI** To make this dish even faster, use matchstick-strip carrots that are available in most supermarket produce sections.

# Spice-Crusted Steak with Wild Mushrooms

SERVES 4

UNDER 20 MINUTES

▲ 1 pound boneless sirloin steak, about ½ inch thick, trimmed

½ teaspoon salt

½ teaspoon coarsely ground black pepper

¼ teaspoon ground coriander

¼ teaspoon ground cumin

2 teaspoons olive oil

▲ 1 small onion, thinly sliced

▲ 1 pound mixed wild mushrooms, sliced

2 teaspoons chopped fresh rosemary

¼ cup dry white wine

PER SERVING (3 slices steak with ½ cup mushrooms): 222 Cal, 7 g Total Fat, 2 g Sat Fat, 0 g Trans Fat, 70 mg Chol, 353 mg Sod, 7 g Carb, 3 g Sugar, 1 g Fib, 29 g Prot, 45 mg Calc.

5 PointsPlus® value

**1** Sprinkle steak with ¼ teaspoon of salt, ¼ teaspoon of pepper, coriander, and cumin. Heat 1 teaspoon of oil in large heavy skillet over medium-high heat. Add beef and cook until instant-read thermometer inserted into center of steak registers 145°F for medium, about 4 minutes on each side. Transfer to plate.

**2** Meanwhile, heat remaining 1 teaspoon oil in large skillet over medium-high heat. Add onion and cook, stirring, until softened, about 5 minutes. Add mushrooms and rosemary; cook, stirring, until mushrooms are browned, about 5 minutes. Add wine and remaining ¼ teaspoon salt and ¼ teaspoon pepper and cook, stirring, until mushrooms are tender, about 2 minutes longer. Cut steak into 12 slices. Serve with mushrooms.

**FYI** This steak and mushroom dish is perfect for serving with roasted asparagus. To make it, lightly spray asparagus spears with nonstick spray. Arrange in a single layer in a medium baking pan and bake in a 400°F oven for 15 to 20 minutes.

SPICE-CRUSTED STEAK
WITH WILD MUSHROOMS
AND LEMON-THYME MASHED
POTATOES, PAGE 269

# Thai Beef and Cabbage Salad

SERVES 4

UNDER 20 MINUTES

1 teaspoon canola oil

▲ 1 pound boneless sirloin steak, about ½ inch thick, trimmed

¼ cup lime juice

2 tablespoons Asian fish sauce

1 teaspoon packed brown sugar

2 teaspoons grated peeled fresh ginger

1 teaspoon chili-garlic sauce

▲ 4 cups thinly sliced Napa cabbage

▲ 2 scallions, thinly sliced

▲ 1 small red bell pepper, thinly sliced

½ cup chopped fresh mint

**PER SERVING (3 slices steak with 1¼ cups salad):**
203 Cal, 6 g Total Fat, 2 g Sat Fat, 0 g Trans Fat, 49 mg Chol, 792 mg Sod, 7 g Carb, 4 g Sugar, 2 g Fib, 28 g Prot, 79 mg Calc.

**1** Heat oil in large skillet over medium-high heat. Add steak and cook until instant-read thermometer inserted into center of steak registers 145°F for medium, 4–5 minutes on each side. Transfer to cutting board and let stand 5 minutes.

**2** Meanwhile, to make dressing, whisk together lime juice, fish sauce, brown sugar, ginger, and chili-garlic sauce in small bowl.

**3** Combine cabbage, scallions, bell pepper, and mint in large bowl. Add 2 tablespoons of dressing and toss to coat. Divide salad evenly among 4 plates.

**4** Cut steak into 12 slices and divide evenly among salads. Drizzle evenly with remaining dressing and serve at once.

**FYI** For more color and a touch of sweetness, you can add 2 coarsely shredded carrots to the salad. And for more flavor, add ¼ cup chopped fresh cilantro with the mint.

# Grilled Steak Soft Tacos

SERVES 4

UNDER 20 MINUTES

▲ 1 (1-pound) flank steak, trimmed
³/₄ teaspoon chili powder
³/₄ teaspoon ground cumin
¹/₄ teaspoon salt
8 (8-inch) fat-free whole wheat tortillas, warmed
▲ 2 cups thinly sliced green cabbage
▲ 1 medium tomato, chopped
▲ ¹/₂ red onion, thinly sliced
¹/₂ cup chopped fresh cilantro
Lime wedges

**PER SERVING (2 tacos):**
310 Cal, 12 g Total Fat, 3 g Sat Fat,
0 g Trans Fat, 42 mg Chol,
745 mg Sod, 30 g Carb, 1 g Sugar,
20 g Fib, 37 g Prot, 43 mg Calc.

**1** Sprinkle steak with chili powder, cumin, and salt. Spray large ridged grill pan with nonstick spray and set over medium-high heat. Place steak on pan and grill until instant-read thermometer inserted into center of steak registers 145°F for medium, about 5 minutes on each side. Transfer steak to cutting board and let rest 5 minutes. Cut steak into 16 slices.

**2** Top each tortilla evenly with steak, cabbage, tomato, onion, and cilantro. Fold each taco in half and serve with lime wedges.

**GRILLED FLANK STEAK WITH TOMATO-FENNEL SALAD**

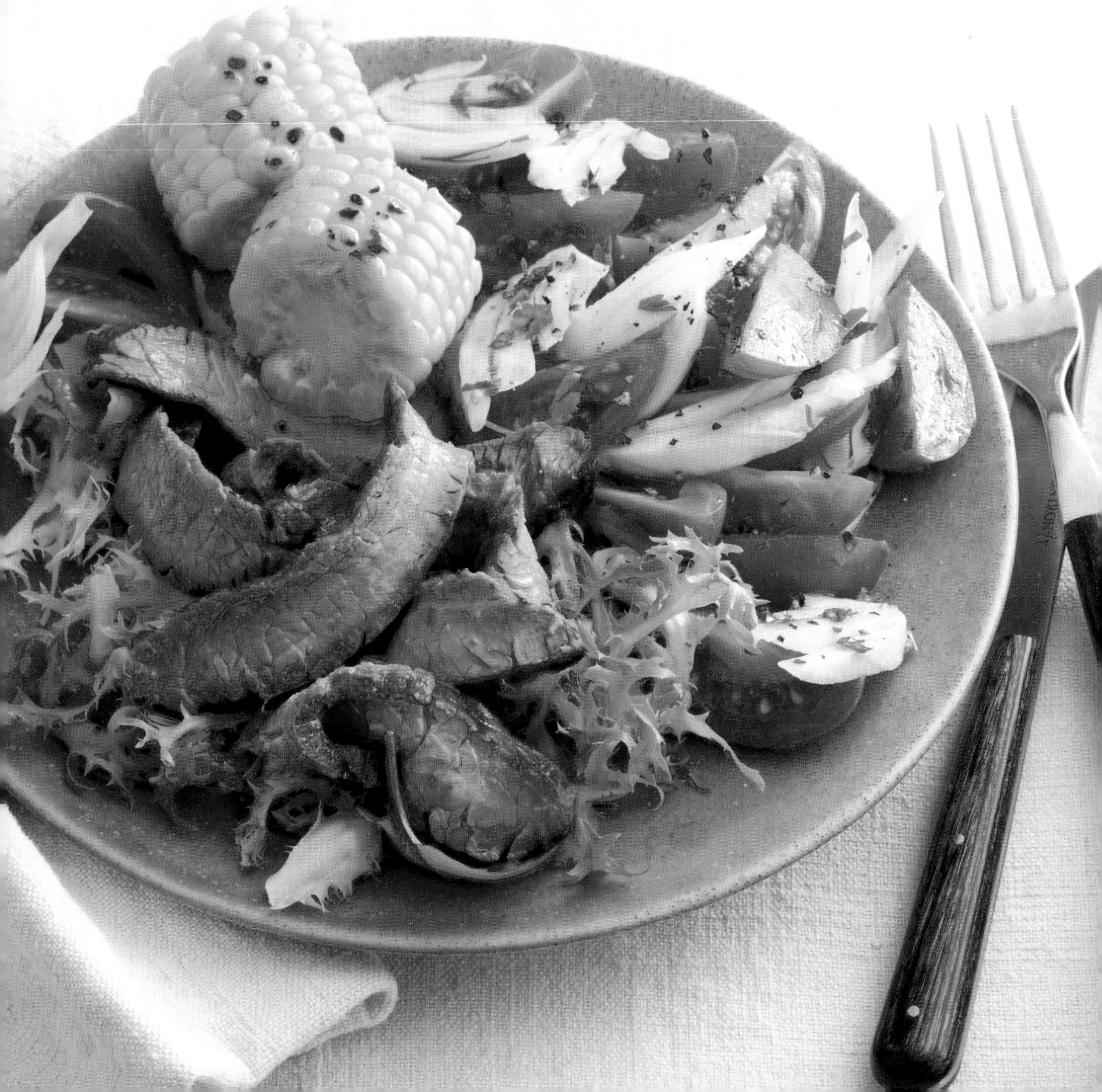

# Grilled Flank Steak with Tomato-Fennel Salad

SERVES 4

UNDER 20 MINUTES

▲ 4 plum tomatoes, each cut into 6 wedges

2 tablespoons chopped fresh flat-leaf parsley

2 teaspoons grated lemon zest

1 tablespoon lemon juice

³/₄ teaspoon salt

¹/₄ teaspoon black pepper

▲ 1 (1-pound) flank steak, trimmed

▲ 1 fennel bulb, cut lengthwise into ¹/₂-inch-thick slices

**PER SERVING (4 slices steak with 1 cup salad):**
191 Cal, 7 g Total Fat, 3 g Sat Fat, 0 g Trans Fat, 42 mg Chol, 519 mg Sod, 7 g Carb, 2 g Sugar, 3 g Fib, 25 g Prot, 55 mg Calc

**1** Spray grill rack with nonstick spray; preheat grill to medium-high or prepare medium-high fire.

**2** Combine tomatoes, parsley, lemon zest and juice, ¹/₄ teaspoon of salt, and ¹/₈ teaspoon of pepper in medium bowl. Set aside.

**3** Sprinkle steak with remaining ¹/₂ teaspoon salt and remaining ¹/₈ teaspoon pepper. Lightly spray fennel with nonstick spray. Place steak and fennel on grill rack. Grill, turning fennel occasionally until fennel is tender and instant-read thermometer inserted into center of steak registers 145°F for medium, about 4–5 minutes on each side. Remove core from fennel; coarsely chop fennel. Stir fennel into tomato mixture. Cut steak into 16 slices and serve with salad.

**FYI** To make this meal more filling and nutritious, serve the steak and salad over a bed of curly endive or mixed baby greens along with corn-on-the-cob (¹/₂ small ear of corn will increase the *PointsPlus* value by *1*).

# Filets Mignons with Orange-Avocado Salad

SERVES 4

UNDER 20 MINUTES

▲ 1 large navel orange

1 small ripe Hass avocado, halved, pitted, peeled and diced

▲ 1 scallion, thinly sliced

▲ ¼ cup diced red bell pepper

2 tablespoons chopped fresh basil

Pinch plus ½ teaspoon salt

Pinch cayenne

▲ 2 large leeks with green tops (optional)

▲ 4 (¼-pound) filet mignon steaks, trimmed

¾ teaspoon ground cumin

¼ teaspoon black pepper

1 teaspoon canola oil

**PER SERVING (1 filet with ½ cup salad):**
255 Cal, 13 g Total Fat, 3 g Sat Fat,
0 g Trans Fat, 67 mg Chol,
382 mg Sod, 8 g Carb, 4 g Sugar,
4 g Fib, 26 g Prot, 44 mg Calc.

**1**  To make salad, grate 1 teaspoon zest from orange and place in medium bowl. With sharp knife, peel orange, removing all white pith. Cut orange into rounds; cut rounds into quarters. Add orange to bowl. Add avocado, scallion, bell pepper, basil, pinch of salt, and cayenne and toss to combine.

**2**  If wrapping steaks in green leek tops, bring medium saucepan of water to boil. Cut green tops off leeks and add to saucepan. Reserve white part of leeks for another use. Cook until softened, 2 minutes. Drain and rinse under cold running water. Wrap steaks with leek tops and tie with kitchen string.

**3**  Sprinkle steaks with remaining ½ teaspoon salt, cumin, and black pepper. Heat oil in large heavy skillet over medium-high heat. Add steaks and cook, until instant-read thermometer inserted into side of steaks registers 145°F for medium, 2–3 minutes on each side. Serve with salad.

**FYI**  You can make an easy and nutritious side dish to accompany the steak and salad by tossing cooked barley with lemon juice, grated lemon zest, chopped fresh basil, and salt and pepper to taste and sprinkle with very thin strips of leek. A ⅔ cup serving of cooked barley will increase the per-serving *PointsPlus* value by *3*.

FILETS MIGNONS WITH
ORANGE-AVOCADO SALAD

▲ **3 cups reduced-sodium chicken broth**

**¹/₄ cup reduced-sodium soy sauce**

**¹/₄ cup mirin**

▲ **¹/₂ pound boneless sirloin steak, trimmed and cut into strips**

▲ **1 small onion, halved and thinly sliced**

▲ **¹/₂ (14-ounce) package firm tofu, drained and cubed**

▲ **1 carrot, coarsely shredded**

▲ **1 yellow bell pepper, thinly sliced**

▲ **4 ounces shiitake mushrooms, stems removed and caps thinly sliced**

▲ **12 ounces fresh bean sprouts**

**PER SERVING (1¹/₂ cups sukiyaki with 1 cup bean sprouts):**
260 Cal, 6 g Total Fat, 2 g Sat Fat,
0 g Trans Fat, 25 mg Chol,
633 mg Sod, 25 g Carb, 12 g Sugar,
4 g Fib, 26 g Prot, 140 mg Calc.

# Beef Sukiyaki

**1**  Bring broth, soy sauce, and mirin to boil in large, deep skillet over high heat. Place steak and onion in separate mounds on each side of skillet. Reduce heat and simmer 3 minutes.

**2**  Add tofu, carrot, bell pepper, and mushrooms in separate mounds around steak and simmer until beef is cooked through and vegetables are crisp-tender, about 5 minutes.

**3**  Divide bean sprouts evenly among 4 serving bowls; top each with one quarter of sukiyaki.

**FYI**  To complete this meal, you can serve the sukiyaki with brown rice. A ²/₃-cup serving will increase the ***PointsPlus*** value by **3**.

# Hoisin Beef and Vegetable Stir-Fry

SERVES 4

UNDER 20 MINUTES

▲ ¹/₃ cup reduced-sodium
chicken broth

2 tablespoons hoisin sauce

1 teaspoon cornstarch

¹/₂ teaspoon Asian (dark) sesame oil

2 teaspoons canola oil

▲ 1 pound boneless sirloin steak,
trimmed and thinly sliced

▲ 4 scallions, cut into 1-inch pieces

▲ 1 cup snow peas, trimmed

▲ 1  red bell pepper, thinly sliced

2 garlic cloves, minced

Pinch red pepper flakes

PER SERVING (1 cup):
207 Cal, 6 g Total Fat, 2 g Sat Fat,
0 g Trans Fat, 50 mg Chol,
194 mg Sod, 9 g Carb, 4 g Sugar,
2 g Fib, 28 g Prot, 43 mg Calc.

**1**  Stir together broth, hoisin sauce, cornstarch, and sesame oil in small bowl until smooth.

**2**  Heat large heavy skillet or wok over medium-high heat until a drop of water sizzles in pan. Add 1 teaspoon canola oil and swirl to coat pan; add steak and stir-fry until browned, about 3 minutes. Transfer to plate.

**3**  Heat remaining 1 teaspoon canola oil in same skillet over medium-high heat and swirl to coat. Add scallions, peas, bell pepper, garlic, and red pepper flakes; stir-fry until vegetables are crisp-tender, about 4 minutes.

**4**  Stir cornstarch mixture and add to skillet; stir-fry until sauce bubbles and thickens, about 1 minute. Return steak to skillet and cook, stirring, until heated through, 1 minute.

**FYI**  To make the stir-fry even more colorful and filling, add more vegetables in step 3. Try 2 cups small broccoli florets, matchstick-strip carrots, sliced bok choy, or sliced mushrooms.

ANCHO BEEF AND
BEAN CHILI

# Ancho Beef and Bean Chili

SERVES 4

2 dried ancho chile peppers, seeded and torn into pieces

2 dried pasilla or New Mexico red chile peppers, seeded and torn into pieces

2 garlic cloves, minced

1½ teaspoons dried oregano

½ teaspoon ground cumin

½ teaspoon salt

¼ teaspoon ground cinnamon

▲ 1 onion, chopped

▲ 1 green bell pepper, chopped

▲ ¾ pound boneless sirloin steak, trimmed and cut into ½-inch cubes

▲ 1½ cups reduced-sodium beef broth

▲ 1¼ cups canned red kidney beans, rinsed and drained

PER SERVING (1¼ cups):
269 Cal, 6 g Total Fat, 2 g Sat Fat, 0 g Trans Fat, 31 mg Chol, 362 mg Sod, 29 g Carb, 5 g Sugar, 12 g Fib, 27 g Prot, 48 mg Calc.

1  Set medium skillet over medium-low heat. Add ancho and pasilla peppers; toast until fragrant, turning occasionally, about 4 minutes. Transfer to medium bowl; add enough boiling water to cover peppers. Let stand 10 minutes. Drain peppers, reserving 2 tablespoons of soaking liquid. Combine peppers, reserved soaking liquid, garlic, oregano, cumin, salt, and cinnamon in mini–food processor or blender and process until smooth.

2  Spray large saucepan with nonstick spray; set over medium heat. Add onion and bell pepper; cook, stirring frequently, until onion softens, about 4 minutes. Add ancho pepper mixture and cook, stirring frequently, until fragrant, about 1 minute. Add steak and cook, stirring frequently, until no longer pink, about 3 minutes.

3  Stir in broth and bring to boil. Reduce heat and simmer, covered, 20 minutes. Stir in beans and simmer, covered, until beef is tender and chili thickens slightly, about 20 minutes.

FYI  To add even more flavor to this chili, you can top each serving with a salsa made with chopped tomatoes, red and yellow bell peppers, scallions, and fresh cilantro tossed with lime juice to taste. Serve with home-baked tortilla strips: Cut 4 (6-inch) whole wheat tortillas into 6 (1-inch) strips. Spray lightly with cooking spray and sprinkle with 1 teaspoon chili powder. Place on a baking sheet and bake at 425°F until crisp, 6 to 8 minutes. Six tortilla strips will increase the *PointPlus* value by *2*.

# Gingery Pepper Steak Stir-Fry

2 teaspoons Asian (dark) sesame oil

▲ 4 scallions, thinly sliced

¼ cup minced peeled fresh ginger

2 garlic cloves, thinly sliced

▲ 1 pound boneless sirloin steak, trimmed and thinly sliced

▲ 2 yellow bell peppers, thinly sliced

▲ 2 green bell peppers, thinly sliced

2 tablespoons reduced-sodium soy sauce

2 tablespoons rice vinegar

2 tablespoons oyster sauce

**PER SERVING** (1⅓ cups):
233 Cal, 8 g Total Fat, 2 g Sat Fat,
0 g Trans Fat, 49 mg Chol,
574 mg Sod, 13 g Carb, 4 g Sugar,
2 g Fib, 28 g Prot, 52 mg Calc.

**1** Heat large heavy skillet or wok over medium-high heat until drop of water sizzles in pan. Add oil and swirl to coat pan. Add scallions, ginger, and garlic; stir-fry until scallions soften, about 1 minute. Add steak and stir-fry until no longer pink, about 3 minutes. Add bell peppers and stir-fry until crisp-tender, about 2 minutes.

**2** Add soy sauce, vinegar, and oyster sauce. Stir-fry until mixture is thickened and bubbling, about 1 minute.

**FYI** Oyster sauce, made from oysters, sugar, and spices, is a popular ingredient in Chinese cooking. It tastes mildly fishy and becomes savory and aromatic once it blends with other ingredients in a stir-fry. Look for it in the Asian section of most supermarkets.

# Hearty Beef and Hominy Chili

SERVES 4

▲ 1 pound ground lean beef
(7% fat or less)

▲ 1 small onion, chopped

▲ 1 small green bell pepper, chopped

▲ 1 jalapeño pepper, seeded
and minced

2 garlic cloves, minced

▲ 1 (14 1/2-ounce) can diced tomatoes

1/4 cup tomato paste

1 tablespoon chili powder

1 teaspoon ground cumin

1 teaspoon dried oregano

1/8 teaspoon salt

▲ 1 (15-ounce) can hominy,
rinsed and drained

2 tablespoons chopped fresh cilantro

PER SERVING (1 1/2 cups):
286 Cal, 7 g Total Fat, 3 g Sat Fat,
0 g Trans Fat, 69 mg Chol,
740 mg Sod, 28 g Carb,9 g Sugar,
6 g Fib, 26 g Prot, 62 mg Calc.

**1** Combine beef, onion, bell pepper, jalapeño, and garlic in Dutch oven and set over medium heat. Cook beef, breaking it up with wooden spoon, until browned, about 6 minutes.

**2** Stir in tomatoes, tomato paste, chili powder, cumin, oregano, and salt; bring to boil. Reduce heat and simmer, partially covered, until chili thickens slightly, about 30 minutes. Stir in hominy and cook until heated through, about 3 minutes. Stir in cilantro just before serving.

**FYI** To add more color to the chili, you can top it with thinly sliced scallions or finely chopped radishes.

# Brunswick Beef Stew

2 teaspoons olive oil

▲ 1 small onion, chopped

▲ ³/₄ pound ground lean beef (7% fat or less)

▲ 2 large tomatoes, chopped

▲ 1 ½ cups frozen sliced okra

▲ 1 cup frozen lima beans

▲ 1 cup frozen corn kernels

2 teaspoons dried thyme

2 teaspoons dried sage

½ teaspoon salt

½ teaspoon black pepper

⅛ teaspoon red pepper sauce

▲ ½ cup reduced-sodium beef broth

**PER SERVING (1 ½ cups):**
275 Cal, 8 g Total Fat, 3 g Sat Fat,
0 g Trans Fat, 51 mg Chol,
480 mg Sod, 28 g Carb, 5 g Sugar,
7 g Fib, 24 g Prot, 122 mg Calc.

**1** Heat oil in large saucepan over medium heat. Add onion and cook, stirring occasionally, until softened, about 3 minutes. Add beef and cook, breaking it up with wooden spoon, until browned, about 5 minutes.

**2** Add tomatoes, okra, lima beans, corn, thyme, sage, salt, pepper, and pepper sauce; cook, stirring frequently, until tomatoes are softened, about 3 minutes. Stir in broth and bring just to boil. Reduce heat and simmer, covered, stirring occasionally, until stew thickens slightly, about 20 minutes.

**FYI** There's no need to defrost the vegetables before you add them to the stew—they'll quickly thaw while cooking with the fresh tomatoes.

# Meatballs and Artichokes Braised in White Wine

SERVES 4

▲ 1 pound ground lean beef (7% fat or less)

¼ cup dried whole wheat bread crumbs

▲ 1 large egg white

1 garlic clove, minced

½ teaspoon paprika

½ teaspoon salt

½ teaspoon black pepper

1 tablespoon olive oil

▲ 1 large leek, halved lengthwise and thinly sliced (white and light green parts only)

1 tablespoon minced fresh rosemary

2 teaspoons grated lemon zest

1 cup dry white wine

2 teaspoons Worcestershire sauce

▲ 1 (9-ounce) package frozen artichoke hearts, thawed

2 teaspoons lemon juice

PER SERVING (4 meatballs, ½ cup vegetables, and 2 tablespoons sauce): 309 Cal, 11 g Total Fat, 3 g Sat Fat, 0 g Trans Fat, 69 mg Chol, 528 mg Sod, 15 g Carb, 2 g Sugar, 5 g Fib, 26 g Prot, 76 mg Calc.

**1** Combine beef, bread crumbs, egg white, garlic, paprika, salt, and pepper in large bowl. Shape into 16 meatballs.

**2** Spray large deep nonstick skillet with nonstick spray and set over medium heat. Add 8 meatballs and cook, turning occasionally, until browned on all sides, about 4 minutes. Transfer to plate. Repeat with remaining 8 meatballs.

**3** Heat oil in same skillet. Add leek and cook, stirring frequently, until softened, about 2 minutes. Stir in rosemary and lemon zest; cook, stirring frequently, until fragrant, about 30 seconds. Add wine and Worcestershire sauce; bring to simmer, scraping up browned bits from bottom of skillet. Add meatballs and artichokes to skillet and simmer, covered, 15 minutes. Stir in lemon juice and simmer, covered, 5 minutes.

**FYI** You can add up to 2 cups of diced carrots, celery, or parsnips when you add the leek. If you do add extra vegetables, add ½ cup reduced-sodium chicken broth along with the wine.

# Greek Beef and Mushroom Pizza

2 teaspoons olive oil

▲ 1 small onion, minced

▲ ½ pound ground lean beef
(7% fat or less)

▲ 1 tomato, chopped

2 tablespoons minced
fresh parsley

1 tablespoon fresh thyme leaves

1 tablespoon minced fresh oregano

1 teaspoon cinnamon

1 teaspoon ancho chile powder

½ teaspoon salt

¼ teaspoon black pepper

1 (10-ounce) prebaked thin whole
wheat pizza crust

▲ 4 ounces shiitake mushrooms,
stems removed and caps
thinly sliced

2 ounces haloumi cheese, grated

Fresh thyme sprigs for garnish
(optional)

**PER SERVING (1 wedge):**
337 Cal, 11 g Total Fat, 4 g Sat Fat,
0 g Trans Fat, 44 mg Chol,
773 mg Sod, 39 g Carb, 3 g Sugar,
6 g Fib, 20 g Prot, 181 mg Calc.

**1** Preheat oven to 400°F. Spray large baking sheet with nonstick spray.

**2** Heat oil in large nonstick skillet over medium heat. Add onion and cook, stirring frequently, until softened, about 3 minutes. Add beef and cook, breaking it up with wooden spoon, until browned, about 5 minutes. Stir in tomato, parsley, thyme, oregano, cinnamon, chile powder, salt, and pepper; cook, stirring occasionally, until thickened, about 2 minutes.

**3** Place pizza crust on baking sheet. Top crust evenly with beef mixture, then with mushrooms and haloumi. Bake until cheese melts and crust is crisp, about 15 minutes. Let stand 5 minutes before serving. Cut into 4 wedges. Top with thyme sprigs (if using).

**FYI** Haloumi, a firm creamy cheese from Cyprus, is made from a combination of sheep and goat milk. If you can't find it, you can use ¼ cup crumbled feta and ¼ cup shredded mozzarella cheese.

# Middle Eastern Meatballs in Tomato Sauce

SERVES 6

▲ 1 pound ground lean beef (7% fat or less)

▲ 1 large onion, chopped

▲ 1 large egg

½ cup bulgur

¼ cup chopped fresh cilantro

3 garlic cloves, minced

1 teaspoon ground cumin

½ teaspoon salt

¼ teaspoon black pepper

2 teaspoons olive oil

▲ 1 (14½-ounce) can diced tomatoes

▲ 1 (8-ounce) can tomato sauce

▲ 1 cup reduced-sodium chicken broth

**PER SERVING** (5 meatballs with 1 cup sauce):
209 Cal, 7 g Total Fat, 2 g Sat Fat,
0 g Trans Fat, 82 mg Chol,
615 mg Sod, 18 g Carb, 5 g Sugar,
4 g Fib, 20 g Prot, 41 mg Calc.

**1** Combine beef, one half of onion, egg, bulgur, cilantro, 1 garlic clove, cumin, ¼ teaspoon of salt, and ⅛ teaspoon of pepper in large bowl. Cover and refrigerate 30 minutes or up to 4 hours. Shape into 30 meatballs.

**2** Heat oil in large deep skillet over medium heat. Add remaining one half of onion and 2 garlic cloves. Cook, stirring frequently, until onion is softened, about 5 minutes. Stir in tomatoes, tomato sauce, broth, and remaining ¼ teaspoon salt and ⅛ teaspoon pepper. Add meatballs and bring to boil. Reduce heat and simmer, covered, until meatballs are cooked through and sauce thickens slightly, about 20 minutes.

**FYI** Whole wheat spaghetti is a must for serving with this dish to soak up all the sauce (½ cup of cooked whole wheat spaghetti will increase the *PointsPlus* value by *2*).

# Roast Pork with Potatoes and Cauliflower

SERVES 4

▲ ½ pound red potatoes, scrubbed and cut into ½-inch cubes

4 garlic cloves (do not peel)

4 teaspoons olive oil

▲ 1 (1-pound) boneless center-cut pork loin, trimmed

½ teaspoon salt

½ teaspoon black pepper

▲ 3 cups cauliflower florets

2 tablespoons minced fresh rosemary or 2 teaspoons dried

1 tablespoon white balsamic vinegar

**PER SERVING (2 slices pork with 1 cup vegetables):**
251 Cal, 11 g Total Fat, 2 g Sat Fat, 0 g Trans Fat, 66 mg Chol, 363 mg Sod, 15 g Carb, 3 g Sugar, 3 g Fib, 24 g Prot, 52 mg Calc.

**1** Preheat oven to 375°F. Place potatoes and garlic in large roasting pan; drizzle with olive oil and toss to coat. Arrange in single layer and roast 15 minutes.

**2** Sprinkle pork on all sides with salt and pepper.

**3** Remove roasting pan from oven. Push potatoes and garlic toward edge of pan; place pork in center of pan. Roast 25 minutes. Remove roasting pan from oven. Place cauliflower around edge of pan; sprinkle with rosemary. Roast until vegetables are tender and instant-read meat thermometer inserted into center of pork registers 145°F, about 10 minutes. Transfer pork to cutting board and let stand 10 minutes.

**4** Meanwhile, transfer vegetables to serving bowl. Set roasting pan over two burners over medium heat. Add vinegar and cook, scraping up browned bits from bottom of pan, until vinegar simmers. Spoon vinegar over vegetables and toss to coat. Cut pork into 8 slices and serve with vegetables.

**FYI** Roasting whole garlic cloves with this dish will scent the vegetables and pork. But don't throw them out; enjoy the mellow flavor of the soft garlic pulp spread on the slices of pork.

ROSEMARY PORK TENDERLOIN
WITH ROOT VEGETABLES

# Rosemary Pork Tenderloin with Root Vegetables

**SERVES 4**

- ▲ 1 (1-pound) pork tenderloin, trimmed
- 1 tablespoon finely chopped fresh rosemary
- ³/₄ teaspoon salt
- ¹/₄ teaspoon black pepper
- 2 teaspoons olive oil
- ▲ 4 carrots, cut into thin strips
- ▲ 3 parsnips, peeled and cut into thin strips
- ▲ 2 medium turnips, peeled and cut into thin strips
- ▲ ³/₄ cup reduced-sodium chicken broth
- 1 garlic clove, minced

**PER SERVING (3 slices pork with 1 cup vegetables):**
278 Cal, 6 g Total Fat, 2 g Sat Fat, 0 g Trans Fat, 62 mg Chol, 593 mg Sod, 31 g Carb, 11 g Sugar, 7 g Fib, 26 g Prot, 94 mg Calc.

**1** Preheat oven to 425°F.

**2** Sprinkle pork with rosemary, ¹/₂ teaspoon of salt, and ¹/₈ teaspoon of pepper. Heat oil in Dutch oven over medium-high heat. Add pork and cook, turning occasionally, until browned on all sides, about 8 minutes. Add carrots, parsnips, turnips, broth, garlic, and remaining ¹/₄ teaspoon salt and ¹/₈ teaspoon pepper.

**3** Transfer Dutch oven to oven and bake, stirring vegetables occasionally, until an instant-read thermometer inserted into center of pork registers 145°F, 10 to 15 minutes. Remove pork from pan; cover loosely with foil. Return vegetables to oven; bake until tender, about 10 minutes. Cut pork into 12 slices. Serve pork with vegetables and any pan juices.

**FYI** To complete this autumn harvest meal, serve steamed Swiss chard tossed with red wine vinegar and salt and pepper to taste.

# Apricot-Bourbon Glazed Pork Tenderloin

SERVES 4

¼ cup apricot preserves

1 tablespoon bourbon

▲ 1 (1-pound) pork tenderloin, trimmed

1 teaspoon ground cumin

½ teaspoon salt

¼ teaspoon black pepper

**PER SERVING (3 slices):**
183 Cal, 3 g Total Fat, 1 g Sat Fat, 0 g Trans Fat, 62 mg Chol, 348 mg Sod, 13 g Carb, 9 g Sugar, 0 g Fib, 23 g Prot, 14 mg Calc.

**1** Spray grill rack with nonstick spray. Preheat grill to medium-high or prepare medium-high fire.

**2** To make glaze, stir together preserves and bourbon in small bowl.

**3** Sprinkle tenderloin with cumin, salt, and pepper. Place tenderloin on grill rack and grill, turning occasionally, 10 minutes.

**4** Continue to grill pork, turning and brushing with glaze, until instant-read thermometer inserted into center of pork registers 145°F, about 5 minutes longer. Transfer to cutting board and let stand 5 minutes. Cut into 12 slices.

**FYI** Serve this simple main dish with quick and easy side dishes. Cook whole wheat couscous according to the package directions and stir in grated lemon zest just before serving. And serve steamed broccoli alongside. A ⅔ cup portion of cooked whole wheat couscous per serving will increase the *PointsPlus* value by *3.*

# Grilled Jerk-Seasoned Pork Chops

SERVES 4

⅓ cup lightly packed
fresh cilantro leaves

▲ 2 scallions, sliced

2 teaspoons chopped peeled
fresh ginger

1 garlic clove, chopped

2 teaspoons canola oil

¼ teaspoon dried thyme

¼ teaspoon salt

Pinch ground allspice

Pinch cayenne

▲ 4 (¼-pound) center-cut boneless
pork loin chops, trimmed

PER SERVING (1 pork chop):
169 Cal, 8 g Total Fat, 2 g Sat Fat,
0 g Trans Fat, 66 mg Chol,
191 mg Sod, 1 g Carb, 0 g Sugar,
0 g Fib, 21 g Prot, 27 mg Calc.

**1** Combine all ingredients except pork chops in food processor; pulse until mixture forms a paste.

**2** Place pork chops in shallow glass dish; add cilantro mixture and turn to coat. Cover and refrigerate at least 30 minutes or up to 2 hours.

**3** Spray large ridged grill pan with nonstick spray and set over medium-high heat. Place pork chops in pan and cook until instant-read thermometer inserted into side of chops registers 145°F, about 2 minutes on each side.

**FYI** While the pork chops marinate, grill some quick-cooking vegetables to serve with the meal. Spray a ridged grill pan with nonstick spray and grill any combination of thinly sliced bell peppers, zucchini, yellow squash, or red onion, turning occasionally, until crisp-tender, 6 to 8 minutes. Toss the vegetables with lime juice, chopped fresh cilantro, and a sprinkle of salt.

# Pork Chops with Ginger-Lime Peach Salsa

SERVES 4

UNDER 20 MINUTES

▲ 3 large peaches, peeled, halved, pitted, and chopped

▲ 1 scallion, thinly sliced

▲ 1 jalapeño pepper, seeded and minced

2 tablespoons chopped fresh cilantro

1 tablespoon lime juice

1 teaspoon grated peeled fresh ginger

Pinch plus ½ teaspoon salt

2 teaspoons packed light brown sugar

1 teaspoon curry powder

1 teaspoon ground cumin

▲ 4 (¼-pound) center-cut boneless pork loin chops, trimmed

PER SERVING (1 pork chop with ½ cup salsa): 211 Cal, 6 g Total Fat, 2 g Sat Fat, 0 g Trans Fat, 66 mg Chol, 373 mg Sod, 16 g Carb, 13 g Sugar, 2 g Fib, 23 g Prot, 37 mg Calc

5 PointsPlus value

**1** To make salsa, combine peaches, scallion, jalapeño, cilantro, lime juice, ginger, and pinch of salt in medium bowl; toss to combine.

**2** Stir together remaining ½ teaspoon salt, brown sugar, curry powder, and cumin in small dish. Rub pork chops with seasoning mixture.

**3** Spray large ridged grill pan with nonstick spray and set over medium-high heat. Place pork chops in pan and cook until instant-read thermometer inserted into side of chops registers 145°F, about 2 minutes on each side. Serve with salsa.

**FYI** To make a complete meal, serve this summery dish with steamed sugar snap peas and cooked quinoa (⅔ cup cooked quinoa for each serving will increase the *PointsPlus* value by *3*).

# Pork Chops with Fig-Cranberry Sauce

SERVES 4

UNDER 20 MINUTES

- ▲ 4 (¼-pound) center-cut boneless pork loin chops, trimmed
- 2 teaspoons unsalted butter
- ▲ ¼ cup minced red onion
- ▲ ½ cup reduced-sodium chicken broth
- ▲ 4 fresh figs, quartered
- ▲ ¼ cup chopped fresh or frozen cranberries
- 2 teaspoons fresh thyme leaves
- 2 teaspoons honey
- ¼ teaspoon salt
- ¼ teaspoon black pepper

**PER SERVING** (1 pork chop with ⅓ cup sauce):
213 Cal, 8 g Total Fat, 3 g Sat Fat, 0 g Trans Fat, 72 mg Chol, 200 mg Sod, 13 g Carb, 10 g Sugar, 2 g Fib, 22 g Prot, 39 mg Calc.

**5** PointsPlus® value

**1**  Spray large nonstick skillet with olive oil nonstick spray and set over medium heat. Add pork and cook until instant-read thermometer inserted into side of each chop registers 145°F, about 2 minutes on each side. Transfer to plate.

**2**  Add butter to skillet and heat 30 seconds. Add onion and cook, stirring frequently, until softened, about 1 minute. Add broth and cook, scraping up browned bits from bottom of skillet, until mixture simmers. Stir in figs, cranberries, thyme, honey, salt, and pepper; increase heat and cook, stirring frequently, until sauce thickens slightly, about 2 minutes. Serve with pork.

**FYI**  If fresh figs are not in season, you can use a thinly sliced pear in this recipe instead.

# Pork Chops and Vegetables with Yellow Curry Sauce

SERVES 4

UNDER 20 MINUTES

2 teaspoons canola oil

▲ 4 (¼-pound) center-cut boneless pork loin chops, about ½ inch thick

▲ 1 medium red onion, chopped

▲ 1 green bell pepper, chopped

▲ 1 red bell pepper, chopped

1½ tablespoons yellow Thai curry paste

▲ ¾ pound cremini mushrooms, sliced

1 cup light (reduced-fat) coconut milk

▲ ¼ cup reduced-sodium chicken broth

2 teaspoons brown sugar

PER SERVING (1 chop with ¾ cup vegetables and sauce): 270 Cal, 12 g Total Fat, 2 g Sat Fat, 0 g Trans Fat, 66 mg Chol, 271 mg Sod, 16 g Carb, 7 g Sugar, 4 g Fib, 25 g Prot, 53 mg Calc.

**1** Heat oil in large skillet over medium-high heat. Add pork and cook until browned, about 1 minute on each side. Transfer to plate.

**2** Add onion and bell peppers to skillet; reduce heat and cook, stirring frequently, until onion begins to soften, about 3 minutes. Add curry paste and cook, stirring frequently, until fragrant, about 30 seconds. Stir in mushrooms, coconut milk, broth, and brown sugar; bring to simmer, scraping up browned bits from bottom of skillet.

**3** Return pork and any accumulated juices to skillet. Reduce heat and simmer, covered, until instant-read thermometer inserted into side of each chop registers 145°F, about 3 minutes.

**FYI** Thai curry pastes come in many varieties, mostly identified by their color. While yellow is often the mildest, it's still fiery hot. Look for packages in which the first ingredient is not chiles but instead aromatics like ginger or galangal. If you're at all concerned about the heat, try only 2 teaspoons of the paste the first time you make this dish.

# Gingery Pork and Pepper Stir-Fry

▲ ²/₃ cup reduced-sodium chicken broth

2 tablespoons reduced-sodium soy sauce

1 tablespoon dry sherry

2 teaspoons cornstarch

2 teaspoons canola oil

▲ ³/₄ pound pork tenderloin, trimmed and cut into ¹/₄ x 1-inch-thick strips

▲ 4 scallions, cut into 1-inch pieces

▲ 1 large red bell pepper, thinly sliced

▲ 1 large yellow bell pepper, thinly sliced

1 tablespoon minced peeled fresh ginger

2 garlic cloves, minced

¹/₄ teaspoon red pepper flakes

**PER SERVING (1¹/₂ cups):**
166 Cal, 5 g Total Fat, 1 g Sat Fat,
0 g Trans Fat, 47 mg Chol,
366 mg Sod, 10 g Carb, 4 g Sugar,
2 g Fib, 19 g Prot, 29 mg Calc.

**1** Stir together broth, soy sauce, sherry, and cornstarch in small bowl until smooth.

**2** Heat large heavy skillet or wok over medium-high heat until drop of water sizzles in pan. Add 1 teaspoon of oil and swirl to coat skillet. Add pork and cook, stirring frequently, until pork is just cooked through, 2–3 minutes. Transfer to plate.

**3** Add remaining 1 teaspoon oil to same skillet and swirl to coat. Add scallions and bell peppers and cook, stirring frequently, until slightly softened, about 4 minutes. Add ginger, garlic, and pepper flakes. Cook, stirring, until fragrant and vegetables are tender, 1–2 minutes.

**4** Stir broth mixture and add to skillet; cook, stirring constantly, until mixture bubbles and thickens. Add pork and cook, stirring occasionally, until heated through, about 2 minutes.

**FYI** Serve this stir-fry over soba noodles to soak up all the spicy sauce (1 cup cooked soba noodles for each serving will increase the *PointsPlus* value by *3*).

Lean Meats  Pork

# Vietnamese Pork Summer Rolls

SERVES 4

2 teaspoons canola oil

▲ 1 small red onion, minced

1 tablespoon minced peeled fresh ginger

½ pound ground lean pork

2 tablespoons dry sherry

1 tablespoon reduced-sodium soy sauce

1 tablespoon Asian fish sauce

1 tablespoon lime juice

1 tablespoon golden raisins, minced

½ teaspoon black pepper

1 tablespoon minced fresh cilantro

▲ 1 cucumber, seeded, and cut into matchstick-thin strips

▲ 1 small red bell pepper, cut into matchstick-thin strips

▲ 1 small yellow bell pepper, cut into matchstick-thin strips

8 (9-inch) round rice paper wrappers

PER SERVING (2 rolls):
201 Cal, 6 g Total Fat, 1 g Sat Fat, 0 g Trans Fat, 33 mg Chol, 622 mg Sod, 22 g Carb, 5 g Sugar, 1 g Fib, 14 g Prot, 39 mg Calc.

1  To make filling, heat oil in large nonstick skillet over medium heat. Add onion and ginger; cook, stirring occasionally, until onion softens, about 3 minutes. Add pork and cook, breaking up pork with wooden spoon, until meat is lightly browned, about 5 minutes. Add sherry, soy sauce, fish sauce, lime juice, raisins, and pepper; cook, stirring frequently, until liquid has almost evaporated, about 10 minutes. Transfer filling to medium bowl; let cool slightly, stirring occasionally, about 10 minutes. Stir in cilantro.

2  Meanwhile, combine cucumber and bell peppers in medium bowl.

3  To assemble rolls, working one at a time, dip rice wrapper in bowl of hot water and place it on clean kitchen towel. Place 2 tablespoons pork filling and ¼ cup vegetable mixture in center of each wrapper. Fold in sides, then roll up to completely enclose filling. Transfer to large plate and cover with plastic wrap to prevent drying. Repeat with remaining wrappers, filling, and vegetables to make a total of 8 rolls.

**FYI**  You can also make the summer rolls with lean ground beef or with skinless ground turkey breast. If you don't have sherry on hand, you can substitute reduced-sodium chicken broth. For a different presentation, serve the rolls on spring green garlic tops or scallions.

# Southwest Pork and Lentil Burgers

SERVES 4

▲ ¼ cup green (French) lentils, picked over and rinsed

▲ ³/₄ pound ground pork tenderloin

▲ 1 roasted red pepper (not oil-packed), drained and minced

2 teaspoons ancho chile powder

2 teaspoons ground cumin

2 teaspoons dried oregano

½ teaspoon salt

**PER SERVING (1 burger):**
162 Cal, 5 g Total Fat, 1 g Sat Fat,
0 g Trans Fat, 50 mg Chol,
418 mg Sod, 9 g Carb, 1 g Sugar,
3 g Fib, 19 g Prot, 41 mg Calc

**1**  Cook lentils according to package directions; drain and transfer to large bowl. Coarsely mash with potato masher or fork. Let stand until cool, about 10 minutes.

**2**  Meanwhile, line bottom of broiler pan with foil. Spray broiler rack with nonstick spray. Preheat broiler.

**3**  Add pork, roasted pepper, chile powder, cumin, oregano, and salt to lentils; stir until well mixed. Form mixture into 4 (½-inch-thick) patties. Place patties on broiler pan. Broil 4 inches from heat until instant-read thermometer inserted into side of each burger registers 160°F, about 4 minutes on each side.

**FYI**  For an extra **3 PointsPlus** value, you can serve each of the burgers between 2 slices reduced-calorie bread and top with ¼ cup fat-free salsa.

# Hunan Lamb Stir-Fry

SERVES 6

UNDER 20 MINUTES

▲ ¼ cup reduced-sodium chicken broth

¼ cup reduced-sodium soy sauce

2 tablespoons rice vinegar

1½ teaspoons chili-garlic sauce

2 teaspoons sugar

2 teaspoons cornstarch

1 tablespoon canola oil

8 chiles de árbol or other small dried red chiles

4 garlic cloves, slivered

2 tablespoons minced peeled fresh ginger

1 pound boneless leg of lamb, trimmed and thinly sliced

▲ 2 yellow bell peppers, thinly sliced

▲ 1 (15-ounce) can baby corn, drained

▲ ½ cup canned bamboo shoots, drained

**PER SERVING (1½ cups):**
312 Cal, 11 g Total Fat, 3 g Sat Fat, 0 g Trans Fat, 79 mg Chol, 449 mg Sod, 26 g Carb, 3 g Sugar, 3 g Fib, 25 g Prot, 29 mg Calc.

**1** Stir together broth, soy sauce, vinegar, chili-garlic sauce, sugar, and cornstarch in small bowl until sugar dissolves. Set aside.

**2** Heat large heavy skillet or wok over medium-high heat until drop of water sizzles in pan. Add oil and swirl to coat skillet. Add chile peppers, garlic, and ginger; stir-fry until fragrant, 30 seconds. Add lamb and stir-fry until no longer pink, about 2 minutes. Add bell peppers, corn, and bamboo shoots; stir-fry until bell peppers are crisp-tender, about 3 minutes.

**3** Stir broth mixture and add to skillet; cook, stirring constantly, until mixture bubbles and thickens, about 2 minutes. Remove and discard chile peppers, if desired.

**FYI** In many Asian stir-fries, particularly in Hunan dishes, whole dried chile peppers are added as a flavoring. Be aware that they are very fiery.

**ROAST LAMB WITH WHEAT BERRY AND ROASTED APPLE SALAD**

# Roast Lamb with Wheat Berry and Roasted Apple Salad

**SERVES 6**

▲ 2 apples, quartered

4 shallots, peeled and halved

2 teaspoons olive oil

1½ pounds boneless leg of lamb, trimmed and tied

½ teaspoon salt

½ teaspoon black pepper

▲ ⅔ cup wheat berries

**PER SERVING (2 slices lamb with ½ cup salad):**
382 Cal, 14 g Total Fat, 5 g Sat Fat, 0 g Trans Fat, 119 mg Chol, 291 mg Sod, 27 g Carb, 8 g Sugar, 3 g Fib, 35 g Prot, 35 mg Calc.

**9 PointsPlus® value**

**1** Preheat oven to 375°F.

**2** Place apples and shallots on large roasting pan; drizzle with oil and toss to coat. Arrange apple mixture around edge of pan. Sprinkle all sides of lamb with salt and pepper; place in center of pan. Roast, stirring apple mixture once, until instant-read meat thermometer inserted into center of lamb registers 145°F for medium, about 50 minutes. Transfer lamb to cutting board and let stand 10 minutes.

**3** Meanwhile, bring wheat berries and large pot of water to boil. Reduce heat and simmer until tender, about 45 minutes. Drain wheat berries and transfer to large bowl.

**4** With slotted spoon, transfer apples and shallots to cutting board and coarsely chop. Skim any fat from pan juices. Add apples, shallots, and pan juices to wheat berries; toss to coat. Remove string from lamb and cut into 12 slices. Serve with wheat berry salad.

**FYI** To add some green veggies, toss 2 cups baby spinach into the wheat berry salad just before serving.

**ROSEMARY LAMB CHOPS WITH
SPRING VEGETABLE SALAD**

# Rosemary Lamb Chops with Spring Vegetable Salad

SERVES 4

▲ 8 ounces small red potatoes

1 teaspoon plus 1 tablespoon olive oil

¾ teaspoon salt

½ teaspoon plus pinch black pepper

▲ 8 (2-ounce) bone-in loin lamb chops, frenched

1 teaspoon chopped fresh rosemary

2 tablespoons balsamic vinegar

2 teaspoons honey

▲ 6 cups mixed salad greens

▲ 1 cup sugar snap peas, trimmed

PER SERVING (2 lamb chops with generous 1 cup salad and 1 potato):
225 Cal, 9 g Total Fat, 2 g Sat Fat,
0 g Trans Fat, 45 mg Chol,
519 mg Sod, 19 g Carb, 7 g Sugar,
3 g Fib, 17 g Prot, 26 mg Calc.

**1** Place potatoes in medium saucepan and add enough water to cover by 1 inch; bring to boil and cook until almost tender, 8 minutes. Drain and rinse under cold running water until cool enough to handle. Cut potatoes in half.

**2** Place potatoes in medium bowl; add 1 teaspoon of the oil, ¼ teaspoon of the salt, and ⅛ teaspoon of the pepper and toss to coat.

**3** Spray large nonstick ridged grill pan with nonstick spray and set over medium-high heat. Add potatoes and cook, turning occasionally until browned and tender, 6-8 minutes. Transfer to plate and keep warm.

**4** Sprinkle lamb with rosemary, ¼ teaspoon of remaining salt, and ¼ teaspoon of remaining pepper. Add lamb to pan and cook until browned and instant-read thermometer inserted in center of each chop registers 145°F for medium, 3–4 minutes on each side. Transfer to plate.

**5** Meanwhile, to make salad, whisk together balsamic vinegar, honey, remaining 1 tablespoon oil, remaining ¼ teaspoon salt, and pinch of pepper in large bowl. Add greens and peas and toss to coat; divide among 4 plates. Top evenly with lamb chops and potatoes.

**FYI** Frenching is the term for removing the fat from rib bones to make an elegant presentation when serving lamb chops. Ask your butcher to do this for you, or you can do it at home by trimming and scraping away all the fat from the bone using a knife with a narrow blade.

# Lamb Burgers with Cucumber-Yogurt Sauce

SERVES 4

UNDER 20 MINUTES

1 pound ground lean lamb

1 tablespoon chopped fresh mint

2 teaspoons minced peeled fresh ginger

1 garlic clove, minced

1 teaspoon ground cumin

½ teaspoon paprika

¼ teaspoon salt

1 teaspoon canola oil

▲ ½ cup plain fat-free yogurt

▲ ¼ English (seedless) cucumber, chopped (½ cup)

4 whole wheat hamburger buns, split and warmed

▲ 4 thick slices beefsteak tomato

▲ 1 cup mixed baby lettuce

▲ 1 cucumber, halved crosswise and thinly sliced lengthwise

**PER SERVING (1 burger):**
301 Cal, 10 g Total Fat, 3 g Sat Fat,
0 g Trans Fat, 64 mg Chol,
435 mg Sod, 27 g Carb, 7 g Sugar,
4 g Fib, 26 g Prot, 138 mg Calc.

**1** Combine lamb, mint, ginger, garlic, cumin, paprika, and salt in medium bowl. With damp hands, shape mixture into 4 (½-inch-thick) patties.

**2** Heat oil in large skillet over medium-high heat. Add patties and cook, turning once, until an instant-read thermometer inserted into side of each patty registers 160°F, about 8 minutes.

**3** Meanwhile, to make sauce, stir together yogurt and cucumber in small bowl.

**4** Place burgers in buns and top evenly with tomato slices, baby lettuce, cucumber slices, and sauce.

**FYI** If you prefer, you can make these burgers with lean ground beef or with ground skinless turkey breast instead of the lamb.

LAMB BURGERS WITH
CUCUMBER-YOGURT SAUCE
AND GREEN BEAN AND ORANGE
SALAD, PAGE 252

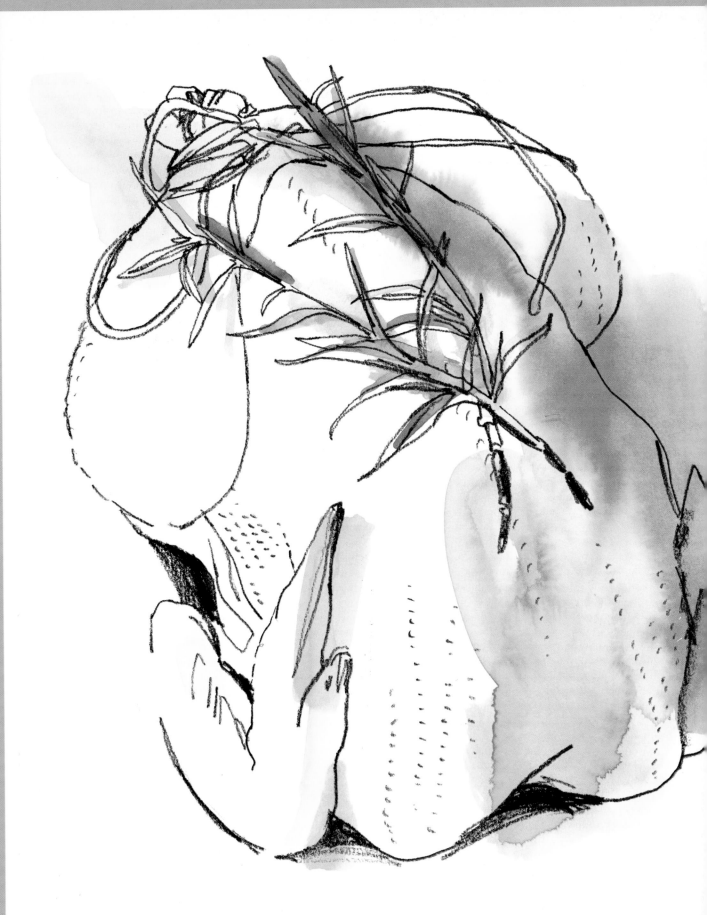

# Lean Poultry

Main Dishes

# Lean Poultry

1 to 2 servings per day of lean protein; 2 to 3 ounces of cooked chicken or turkey counts as 1 serving.

## WHY THEY'RE ESSENTIAL

**Bone up on lean protein.** Studies have shown that people who eat enough protein have less bone loss than those with inadequate protein intakes.

**Poultry is full of phosphorous.** Dairy foods are a great source of phosphorous, but lean poultry is too. This essential mineral regulates energy metabolism and is vital for healthy teeth and bones.

**Lean poultry is naturally good for you.** Chicken and turkey breast contain the same complete package of amino acids as red meat, but may have less fat and saturated fat than beef or pork depending on the cut.

## WHAT TO BUY

**Skinless chicken breast, skinless chicken drumsticks:** For convenience, buy them already skinned.
*TIP: When you find these staples on sale, buy several pounds and package and freeze them in individual meal portions.*

Here's a guide to the types of chicken you'll find in most supermarkets.

REGULAR CHICKEN: Hens are kept in light- and temperature-controlled cages and fed a diet of non-organic grains.

FREE-RANGE CHICKEN: The birds are raised indoors with access to an outdoor area.

ORGANIC CHICKEN: Chickens are fed a diet that is grown organically and are not treated with antibiotics and they are also free-range.

NATURAL CHICKEN: Birds are raised indoors and are processed and packaged without adding artificial ingredients or preservatives. The birds may or may not have been fed organic feed.

**Skinless turkey breast cutlets:** These are perfectly portioned and make quick and convenient lunches and dinners.

*TIP: Marinate with a splash of reduced-sodium soy sauce along with minced garlic and ginger for a delicious Asian meal.*

**Deli-sliced turkey breast and chicken breast:** Keep these on hand to use for healthy sandwiches, salads, and snacks for the whole family.

*TIP: Choose lower sodium versions when available.*

**Canned chunk breast of chicken and chunk white turkey:** These pantry staples can be stored for up to a year, so they're great to have on hand for a quick lunch.

*TIP: Keep a couple of the larger size cans on hand for making an easy soup or salad for the whole family.*

## GOOD TO KNOW

**Portion your poultry.** Turkey cutlets are usually sold in 4-ounce portions. Not so with chicken breast. Check the weight of skinless chicken breast; most are 8 to 10 ounces each. Some producers package them in individually wrapped 4- or 5-ounce portions, which cost a little more, but they're worth it for the convenience.

**Poultry is a *PointsPlus* bargain.** A 3-ounce portion of boneless cooked chicken breast, chicken leg, or turkey breast has a *PointsPlus* value of **3**.

## Skinless chicken breast, skinless turkey breast, and skinless chicken drumsticks

### POWER-UP IDEAS

- Chicken breast doesn't have to be boring. Make a plan to try a new recipe every week.

- Chicken and turkey breast are very lean, so cook them just until they are done to enjoy a moist, juicy dinner.

- Chicken drumsticks stay moist even after long cooking times, so they are great for roasting or cooking in a slow cooker.

### TAKE NOTE

- Chicken provides B vitamins, which helps the body with energy metabolism.

- Rinsing chicken or turkey before cooking spreads bacteria; any bacteria will be destroyed with proper cooking.

- To check for doneness, pierce chicken with a fork; the juices should be clear with no sign of pink.

## Ground skinless chicken breast and turkey breast

### POWER-UP IDEAS

- Use to make leaner versions of your favorite ground beef recipes.

- If your family isn't used to the flavor of lean ground poultry, mix it with half lean ground beef in recipes.

- These lean cuts are perfect for dishes with a sauce or a broth such as lasagna, meatballs with tomato sauce, or chili.

### TAKE NOTE

- Check the label to make sure it says ground skinless chicken or turkey breast. Dark meat and skin mean more fat and calories.

- Even a nonstick skillet needs a coating of nonstick spray before cooking chicken or turkey burgers to prevent them from sticking.

- Always cook ground poultry to an internal temperature of 165°F; it should have no sign of pink.

## Deli-sliced chicken breast and turkey breast and canned chunk breast of chicken and chunk white turkey

### POWER-UP IDEAS

- Use these convenient, ready-to-serve foods for salads, sandwiches, wraps, and quesadillas.

- When pressed for time, use deli turkey or canned turkey or chicken to make enchiladas, soups, or chilis.

- Have an ounce of one of these with a handful of baby carrots for a satisfying protein-rich afternoon snack.

### TAKE NOTE

- When possible, choose the lower sodium versions of these convenient foods.

- Always drain the liquid when using canned meats to reduce the amount of sodium.

- When buying deli turkey, make sure the label says "breast"; otherwise it may contain dark meat and/or skin.

## In this chapter

# Fennel-Orange Roasted Chicken with Potatoes and Green Beans

SERVES 6

1 whole chicken (3½ to 4 pounds) cut up

▲ 1¼ pounds red potatoes, scrubbed and cut into 2-inch chunks

▲ 1 large red onion, cut into 8 wedges

▲ 1 fennel bulb, cut into 8 wedges

4 teaspoons olive oil

½ teaspoon salt

½ teaspoon black pepper

1 tablespoon fennel seeds, crushed

1 teaspoon grated orange zest

▲ ½ pound green beans, trimmed

▲ ½ cup reduced-sodium chicken broth

¼ cup water

PER SERVING (⅙ of chicken, 1 cup vegetables, and 2 tablespoons pan juices): 285 Cal, 8 g Total Fat, 2 g Sat Fat, 0 g Trans Fat, 89 mg Chol, 328 mg Sod, 24 g Carb, 3 g Sugar, 5 g Fib, 31 g Prot, 78 mg Calc.

**7** PointsPlus® value

1　Preheat oven to 450°F. Remove and discard skin and wings from chicken.

2　Place potatoes, onion, and fennel bulb in large roasting pan. Drizzle with 2 teaspoons of oil, sprinkle with ¼ teaspoon of salt and ¼ teaspoon of pepper and toss to coat. Arrange vegetable mixture around edge of pan. Stir together fennel seeds, orange zest, and remaining 2 teaspoons oil, ¼ teaspoon salt, and ¼ teaspoon pepper in small bowl. Place chicken in center of pan and rub seasoning mixture on all sides of chicken. Arrange chicken, skin side up, in single layer in center of pan.

3　Roast 20 minutes. Remove roasting pan from oven. Stir the vegetables and add the green beans. Roast until chicken is cooked through and vegetables are tender, 20–25 minutes.

4　With slotted spoon, transfer chicken and vegetables to platter. Skim any fat from pan juices. Set roasting pan over two burners over medium heat. Add broth and water and cook, scraping up browned bits from bottom of pan, until liquid is reduced to ¾ cup, about 1 minute. Serve with chicken and vegetables.

**FYI**　If you don't have a spice grinder, the easiest way to crush the fennel seeds is to place them in a heavy-duty zip-close plastic bag and roll over the bag with a rolling pin.

# Crispy Thai-Style Chicken with Ginger Bok Choy

SERVES 4

▲ 1 scallion, finely chopped

¼ cup Thai garlic-chili pepper sauce

2 tablespoons Thai roasted red chili paste

1½ teaspoons grated peeled fresh ginger plus 6 thin slices peeled fresh ginger

1 teaspoon Asian (dark) sesame oil

▲ 4 (7-ounce) skinless bone-in chicken breasts

1 cup whole wheat panko bread crumbs

2 tablespoons seasoned rice vinegar

▲ 6 baby bok choy, each cut lengthwise in half

▲ ⅓ cup reduced-sodium chicken broth

PER SERVING (1 breast with 3 pieces bok choy):
311 Cal, 7 g Total Fat, 1 g Sat Fat, 0 g Trans Fat, 89 mg Chol, 974 mg Sod, 25 g Carb, 4 g Sugar, 3 g Fib, 38 g Prot, 20 mg Calc.

**1** Line large rimmed baking pan with foil; spray foil with nonstick spray. Stir together scallion, pepper sauce, chili paste, grated ginger, and sesame oil in small bowl. Arrange chicken in single layer in pan; brush with ¼ cup of sauce mixture. Top evenly with panko, pressing lightly so it adheres. Stir vinegar into remaining sauce mixture; drizzle evenly over panko until absorbed. Let chicken stand at room temperature 15 minutes.

**2** Preheat oven to 500°F.

**3** Roast chicken until crumbs are browned and instant-read thermometer inserted into each breast registers 165°F, 25–30 minutes.

**4** Meanwhile, place bok choy, cut side down, in large skillet. Add broth and sliced ginger; bring to boil. Reduce heat and simmer, covered, 3 minutes. Uncover and simmer until bok choy is tender and broth evaporates, about 2 minutes. Remove and discard ginger. Serve chicken with bok choy.

**FYI** For a sweet accompaniment with this dish, you can add four plums, halved and pitted, to the pan with the chicken during the last 10 minutes of roasting.

# Grilled Chicken with Minty Melon-Feta Salad

1 tablespoon olive oil

1 tablespoon minced fresh oregano or 1 teaspoon dried oregano

1 ¼ teaspoons grated lime zest

1 garlic clove, minced

¼ teaspoon salt

¼ teaspoon black pepper

▲ 4 (7-ounce) skinless bone-in chicken breasts

▲ 2 ½ cups cubed cantaloupe

▲ 2 ½ cups cubed honeydew melon

2 tablespoons chopped fresh mint

1 tablespoon lime juice

▲ 1 jalapeño pepper, seeded and minced

½ cup crumbled low-fat feta cheese

Lime wedges

**PER SERVING (1 chicken breast with 1 cup salad):**
316 Cal, 10 g Total Fat, 3 g Sat Fat, 0 g Trans Fat, 94 mg Chol, 493 mg Sod, 20 g Carb, 16 g Sugar, 2 g Fib, 38 g Prot, 91 mg Calc.

1  Spray grill rack with nonstick spray. Preheat grill to medium or prepare medium fire.

2  Combine oil, oregano, 1 teaspoon of lime zest, garlic, salt, and pepper in large bowl; add chicken and turn to coat. Place chicken on grill rack; cover and grill, turning occasionally, until chicken is cooked through, about 25 minutes.

3  Meanwhile, to make salad, stir together cantaloupe, honeydew, mint, lime juice, jalapeño, and remaining ¼ teaspoon lime zest in large bowl. Add feta and toss to combine. Serve chicken with salad and lime wedges.

**FYI**  To make a grilled side dish, cut 4 small leeks in half lengthwise and lightly spray with nonstick spray. Grill, turning occasionally, until lightly browned and tender, 6–8 minutes. Sprinkle with lime juice, salt, and pepper.

GRILLED CHICKEN WITH
MINTY MELON-FETA SALAD

# Chicken with Roasted Red Pepper-Basil Sauce

▲ 1 (7-ounce) jar roasted red peppers, drained (not oil packed),

1 tablespoon balsamic vinegar

1 garlic clove, chopped

³/₄ teaspoon salt

4 tablespoons chopped fresh basil

▲ 4 (5-ounce) skinless boneless chicken breasts

¹/₂ teaspoon black pepper

2 teaspoons olive oil

PER SERVING (1 chicken breast and 2 tablespoons sauce): 189 Cal, 6 g Total Fat, 1 g Sat Fat, 0 g Trans Fat, 78 mg Chol, 634 mg Sod, 3 g Carb, 2 g Sugar, 0 g Fib, 29 g Prot, 26 mg Calc.

**5** PointsPlus® value

1   To make sauce, combine roasted peppers, vinegar, garlic, and ¹/₄ teaspoon of salt in blender or food processor and puree. Scrape mixture into small saucepan and set over medium heat. Cook, stirring frequently, until sauce just begins to simmer. Remove from heat and stir in 2 tablespoons of basil. Keep warm.

2   Meanwhile, sprinkle chicken with remaining 2 tablespoons basil, remaining ¹/₂ teaspoon salt, and black pepper. Heat oil in large skillet over medium-high heat. Add chicken and cook until browned and cooked through, 4–5 minutes on each side. Serve with sauce.

**FYI**  You can complement this easy, elegant entrée by serving it with steamed green beans and whole wheat linguine (¹/₂ cup cooked whole wheat linguine will increase the *PointsPlus* value by *2*).

# Chicken with Red Chile Onions

▲ 4 (5-ounce) skinless boneless chicken breasts

¼ teaspoon salt

2 teaspoons olive oil

▲ 2 red onions, thinly sliced

2 teaspoons minced peeled fresh ginger

1 garlic clove, minced

▲ ½ cup reduced-sodium chicken broth

2 teaspoons red-wine vinegar

1 teaspoon chili-garlic paste

**PER SERVING** (1 chicken breast and ¼ cup onions):
201 Cal, 6 g Total Fat, 1 g Sat Fat, 0 g Trans Fat, 78 mg Chol, 254 mg Sod, 6 g Carb, 3 g Sugar, 1 g Fib, 30 g Prot, 29 mg Calc.

1 Sprinkle chicken with salt. Heat oil in large skillet over medium-high heat. Add chicken and cook until browned and cooked through, 4–5 minutes on each side. Transfer to plate.

2 Add onions, ginger, and garlic to skillet; cook, stirring frequently, until onions begin to soften, about 3 minutes. Stir in broth, vinegar, and chili-garlic paste and cook, stirring constantly, until fragrant, about 30 seconds. Increase heat to high and cook, stirring frequently, until most of liquid is evaporated, 4 minutes longer.

3 Stir any accumulated juices from chicken into skillet. Top chicken evenly with onion mixture.

**FYI** For an instant accompaniment, serve some frozen steam-in-the-bag mixed vegetables—just be sure to choose a variety without a sauce.

**SKILLET CHICKEN WITH
ARTICHOKES AND
ROASTED RED PEPPERS**

# Skillet Chicken with Artichokes and Roasted Red Peppers

SERVES 6

▲ 12 ounces whole wheat penne

▲ ³/₄ pound skinless boneless chicken breast, cut into 1-inch pieces

¹/₂ teaspoon salt

¹/₄ teaspoon black pepper

4 teaspoons olive oil

▲ 1 medium onion, sliced

3 garlic cloves, minced

▲ 1 (14-ounce) can artichoke hearts, drained, patted dry, and quartered

▲ 1 (12-ounce) jar roasted red peppers, drained and sliced (not oil packed)

¹/₃ cup dry white wine

▲ 1 cup reduced-sodium chicken broth

4 tablespoons shredded Parmesan cheese

¹/₄ cup chopped fresh basil

**PER SERVING (1¹/₂ cups):**
385 Cal, 7 g Total Fat, 2 g Sat Fat, 0 g Trans Fat, 34 mg Chol, 667 mg Sod, 53 g Carb, 5 g Sugar, 6 g Fib, 23 g Prot, 83 mg Calc.

9 PointsPlus© value

1  Cook penne according to package directions omitting salt, if desired. Drain and transfer to large bowl.

2  Meanwhile, sprinkle chicken with ¹/₄ teaspoon of salt and ¹/₈ teaspoon of pepper. Heat 2 teaspoons of oil in large skillet over medium heat. Add chicken and cook, turning occasionally, until lightly browned and just cooked through, 3–4 minutes. Transfer to plate and set aside.

3  Heat remaining 2 teaspoons oil in same skillet over medium-high heat. Add onion and garlic. Cook, stirring occasionally, until onion begins to soften, about 2 minutes. Stir in artichoke hearts and roasted peppers. Cook, stirring, about 1 minute. Add wine and cook until liquid is reduced by half, about 1 minute. Stir in broth and bring to a simmer.

4  Add pasta to skillet and cook, stirring occasionally, until heated through and liquid thickens slightly, about 2 minutes. Add chicken and remaining ¹/₄ teaspoon salt and ¹/₈ teaspoon pepper. Cook until chicken is heated through, about 1 minute. Remove from heat and stir in 2 tablespoons cheese and basil. Divide chicken mixture among 4 serving plates; top evenly with remaining 2 tablespoons of cheese.

# Baked Chicken Packets with Zucchini and Tomatoes

SERVES 4

▲ 4 (5-ounce) skinless boneless chicken breasts

¼ teaspoon salt

¼ teaspoon black pepper

▲ 2 cups cubed zucchini

▲ 4 plum tomatoes, each cut into 6 wedges

8 Kalamata olives, pitted and sliced

¼ cup chopped fresh basil

▲ 4 teaspoons reduced-sodium chicken broth or water

**PER SERVING (1 chicken breast with ²/₃ cup vegetables):** 195 Cal, 6 g Total Fat, 1 g Sat Fat, 0 g Trans Fat, 78 mg Chol, 346 mg Sod, 5 g Carb, 3 g Sugar, 2 g Fib, 30 g Prot, 37 mg Calc.

**5** PointsPlus value

1 Preheat oven to 450°F. Cut 4 (12-inch) sheets of foil or parchment paper.

2 Sprinkle chicken with salt and ⅛ teaspoon of pepper. Place 1 chicken breast half on each sheet of foil.

3 Toss together zucchini, tomatoes, olives, basil, and remaining ⅛ teaspoon pepper in medium bowl. Arrange vegetable mixture evenly over chicken. Sprinkle 1 teaspoon broth over each. Crimp foil into packets, making tight seal.

4 Place packets on rimmed baking sheet and bake until chicken is cooked through and squash is tender, about 35 minutes. Let packets stand 5 minutes, then open with care to avoid steam. Transfer chicken and vegetables to plates and drizzle with juices.

**FYI** Serve the packets with whole wheat couscous to soak up the cooking juices from the vegetables (²/₃ cup cooked whole wheat couscous per serving will increase the *PointsPlus* value by *3*).

# Chicken and Green Chile Stew

SERVES 4

▲ 1 pound skinless boneless chicken breasts, cut into 1-inch pieces

¹/₂ teaspoon ground cumin

¹/₄ teaspoon salt

¹/₈ teaspoon black pepper

4 teaspoons olive oil

▲ 1 medium onion, chopped

▲ 1 red bell pepper, chopped

▲ 1 celery stalk, chopped

1 garlic clove, minced

▲ 2 cups reduced-sodium chicken broth

▲ 8 ounces small red potatoes, cut into 1-inch pieces

▲ 1 (4¹/₂-ounce) can chopped green chiles

¹/₄ cup lightly packed fresh cilantro leaves

PER SERVING (generous 1 cup): 252 Cal, 8 g Total Fat, 2 g Sat Fat, 0 g Trans Fat, 63 mg Chol, 383 mg Sod, 18 g Carb, 4 g Sugar, 3 g Fib, 27 g Prot, 54 mg Calc.

**1**  Sprinkle chicken with cumin, salt, and pepper. Heat 2 teaspoons of oil in large saucepan over medium heat. Add chicken, and cook, stirring frequently, until chicken is lightly browned and cooked through, 3–4 minutes. Transfer to plate.

**2**  Add remaining 2 teaspoons oil to saucepan. Add onion, bell pepper, celery, and garlic and cook, stirring frequently, until vegetables are softened, 5 minutes.

**3**  Add broth, potatoes, and chiles to saucepan; increase heat to medium-high and bring to boil. Reduce heat and simmer, covered, stirring occasionally, until potatoes are fork-tender, about 10 minutes. Return chicken to saucepan and cook, stirring constantly, just until heated through, about 1 minute longer. Stir in cilantro.

**FYI**  To make the stew more colorful and nutritious, top each serving with diced tomatoes and thinly sliced scallions.

ROASTED GARLIC CHICKEN AND
VEGETABLES WITH FETTUCCINE

# Roasted Garlic Chicken and Vegetables with Fettuccine

SERVES 6

1 pound boneless skinless chicken thighs, cut into 1-inch pieces

▲ 2 small red or yellow bell peppers, sliced

▲ 1 small fennel bulb, sliced

▲ 1 medium red onion, sliced

▲ 8 ounces asparagus, trimmed and cut into 2-inch pieces

▲ ½ (8-ounce) package cremini mushrooms, quartered

12 garlic cloves (do not peel)

1 tablespoon olive oil

¼ teaspoon salt

¼ teaspoon red pepper flakes

▲ 12 ounces whole wheat fettuccine

▲ 1 (14-ounce) can reduced-sodium chicken broth

½ cup fresh basil leaves, thinly sliced

PER SERVING (2 cups):
405 Cal, 10 g Total Fat, 2 g Sat Fat,
0 g Trans Fat, 50 mg Chol,
205 mg Sod, 54 g Carb, 5 g Sugar,
8 g Fib, 25 g Prot, 94 mg Calc.

1  Preheat oven to 425°F.

2  Place chicken, bell peppers, fennel, onion, asparagus, mushrooms, and garlic in large roasting pan. Drizzle with oil, sprinkle with salt and pepper flakes and toss to coat. Roast, stirring occasionally, until chicken is cooked through and vegetables are tender, 35–40 minutes. Remove garlic from roasting pan. Transfer chicken and vegetables to large bowl and cover to keep warm.

3  Meanwhile, cook fettuccine according to package directions, omitting salt, if desired. Drain and keep warm.

4  Squeeze garlic pulp into roasting pan. Add broth to roasting pan and set pan over two burners over medium-high heat. Cook, scraping up browned bits from bottom of pan and mashing garlic, until liquid is reduced to 1 cup, about 5 minutes. Add broth mixture, pasta, and basil to chicken mixture and toss to combine. Serve at once.

FYI  You can add ½ pound broccolini, trimmed and cut into 1½-inch pieces, to the vegetable mixture before roasting. After roasting, for extra flavor and color, toss in 1 cup cherry tomatoes.

# Chicken and Asparagus Stir-Fry with Basil

SERVES 4

UNDER 20 MINUTES

▲ ³/4 cup reduced-sodium chicken broth

3 tablespoons reduced-sodium soy sauce

1 tablespoon cornstarch

4 teaspoons canola oil

▲ 1 pound skinless boneless chicken breasts, cut into thin strips

2 garlic cloves, minced

1 tablespoon minced peeled fresh ginger

▲ 1 pound asparagus, trimmed and cut into 1-inch pieces

▲ 1 small red or yellow bell pepper, thinly sliced

▲ 2 scallions, cut into 1-inch pieces

¹/4 cup chopped fresh basil

**PER SERVING (1¹/2 cups):**
218 Cal, 8 g Total Fat, 1 g Sat Fat, 0 g Trans Fat, 63 mg Chol, 473 mg Sod, 10 g Carb, 3 g Sugar, 3 g Fib, 27 g Prot, 52 mg Calc.

1   Whisk together broth, soy sauce, and cornstarch in small bowl until smooth.

2   Heat large heavy skillet or wok over medium-high heat until drop of water sizzles in pan. Pour in 2 teaspoons oil and swirl to coat pan. Add chicken and stir-fry until browned and cooked through, about 4 minutes. Transfer chicken to plate.

3   Heat remaining 2 teaspoons oil in same pan. Add garlic and ginger and stir-fry until fragrant, 30 seconds. Add asparagus, bell pepper, and scallions; stir-fry until vegetables are crisp-tender, about 2 minutes. Return chicken to pan. Re-whisk broth mixture and add to pan. Cook, stirring constantly, until mixture bubbles and thickens, about 1 minute. Remove from heat and stir in basil.

FYI  **If asparagus is not in season, you can make this stir-fry with 3 cups of small broccoli florets instead.**

# Chicken Mole Soft Tacos

SERVES 4

1 teaspoon canola oil

▲ 1 large onion, chopped

2 garlic cloves, minced

1 tablespoon unsweetened cocoa

1 teaspoon chili powder

1 teaspoon ground cumin

½ teaspoon cinnamon

½ teaspoon sugar

½ teaspoon dried oregano

⅛ teaspoon salt

▲ 1 (14½-ounce) can no-salt-added diced tomatoes

▲ 1 (15½-ounce) can no-salt-added black beans, rinsed and drained

▲ 1 cup chopped cooked skinless chicken breast

8 (6-inch) whole wheat tortillas, warmed

▲ 2 cups shredded romaine lettuce

½ cup shredded reduced-fat Monterey Jack cheese

**PER SERVING** (2 tacos):
373 Cal, 10 g Total Fat, 2 g Sat Fat, 0 g Trans Fat, 37 mg Chol, 938 mg Sod, 52 g Carb, 5 g Sugar, 25 g Fib, 35 g Prot, 303 mg Calc.

1  Heat oil in large skillet over medium heat. Add onion and garlic; cook, stirring frequently, until golden, about 7 minutes. Add cocoa, chili powder, cumin, cinnamon, sugar, oregano, and salt; cook, stirring constantly, until fragrant, about 1 minute.

2  Add tomatoes; bring to boil. Reduce heat and simmer, stirring occasionally, until slightly thickened, about 8 minutes. Stir in beans and chicken; return to simmer and cook about 3 minutes.

3  Lay tortillas on work surface and spoon about ⅓ cup of chicken mixture down middle of each tortilla; sprinkle chicken evenly with lettuce and cheese. Fold tortillas in half and serve at once.

**FYI**  You can add some crunchy fresh vegetables to the tacos. Top them with sliced radishes, cucumbers, or scallions along with the lettuce.

**COCONUT-CURRY MARINATED
CHICKEN KEBABS**

# Coconut-Curry Marinated Chicken Kebabs

▲ **1 pound skinless boneless chicken breast, cut into 1½-inch chunks**

**⅓ cup light coconut milk**

**1 tablespoon packed light brown sugar**

**1 tablespoon lime juice**

**1 tablespoon garam masala**

**1 teaspoon Thai red curry paste**

**½ teaspoon salt**

**PER SERVING (1 skewer):**
157 Cal, 4 g Total Fat, 1 g Sat Fat,
0 g Trans Fat, 63 mg Chol,
395 mg Sod, 6 g Carb, 3 g Sugar,
1 g Fib, 23 g Prot, 23 mg Calc.

1  Place chicken, coconut milk, brown sugar, lime juice, garam masala, curry paste, and salt in large zip-close plastic bag. Squeeze out air and seal bag; turn to coat chicken. Refrigerate, turning bag occasionally, at least 1 hour or up to 4 hours.

2  If using wooden skewers, soak in water 30 minutes. Spray grill rack with nonstick spray. Preheat grill to medium-high or prepare medium-high fire.

3  Thread chicken onto 4 (8-inch) wooden or metal skewers. Place skewers on grill rack and grill, turning occasionally, until chicken is cooked through, 8–10 minutes.

**FYI**  To add some vegetables to the meal, include pieces of yellow, red, and orange bell peppers on the skewers. You can also make extra vegetable skewers using thin zucchini strips, cherry tomatoes, red onion wedges, and baby onions.

# Citrus Chicken Salad with Sorrel and Sweet Almonds

SERVES 4

UNDER 20 MINUTES

▲ 2 navel oranges

▲ 1 red grapefruit

2 tablespoons white balsamic vinegar

2 teaspoons extra-virgin olive oil

½ teaspoon minced fresh thyme

¼ teaspoon salt

▲ 2 cups shredded cooked skinless chicken breast

▲ 6 ounces red sorrel or baby spinach

▲ 1 head red or white Belgian endive, sliced

▲ 1 scallion, sliced

¼ cup honey-roasted sliced almonds

**PER SERVING (3 cups):**
297 Cal, 10 g Total Fat, 2 g Sat Fat, 0 g Trans Fat, 60 mg Chol, 308 mg Sod, 28 g Carb, 13 g Sugar, 10 g Fib, 27 g Prot, 176 mg Calc.

**1** Grate zest from one half of 1 orange and place in small bowl. Peel and section oranges and grapefruit, adding 2 tablespoons of the citrus juice to the orange zest. Place citrus sections in large bowl.

**2** To make dressing, whisk vinegar, oil, thyme, and salt into citrus zest mixture.

**3** Add chicken, sorrel, endive, and scallion to citrus sections; drizzle with dressing and toss to coat. Sprinkle salad with almonds and serve at once.

**FYI** To make this salad even more colorful and nutritious, toss in 1 cup of fresh raspberries just before serving.

CITRUS CHICKEN SALAD WITH
SORREL AND SWEET ALMONDS

# Chicken Fried Rice

1 tablespoon tomato paste

1 tablespoon Asian fish sauce

3 teaspoons canola oil

▲ 2 large eggs, lightly beaten

▲ 3 scallions, thinly sliced

2 garlic cloves, minced

2 teaspoons minced peeled
fresh ginger

▲ 1½ cups diced cooked skinless
chicken breast

▲ 1 (8.8-ounce) package cooked
brown rice (about 1¾ cups)

▲ 2 plum tomatoes, chopped

2 tablespoons chopped fresh cilantro

**1** Whisk together tomato paste and fish sauce in small bowl until smooth; set aside.

**2** Heat large heavy skillet or wok over medium heat until a drop of water sizzles in pan. Add 1 teaspoon of oil and swirl to coat pan. Add eggs. Stir-fry until firm, about 2 minutes. Transfer scrambled eggs to plate.

**3** Heat remaining 2 teaspoons oil in same skillet. Add scallions, garlic, and ginger and stir-fry until softened, about 3 minutes. Add chicken and rice; stir-fry until rice is coated, about 1 minute. Add tomatoes and tomato paste mixture; stir-fry until tomatoes are softened, about 2 minutes. Remove from heat; stir in eggs and cilantro. Serve at once.

**FYI** **Instead of chicken breast, try this recipe with diced cooked turkey breast, pork loin, or shrimp.**

PER SERVING (1 cup):
240 Cal, 8 g Total Fat, 2 g Sat Fat,
0 g Trans Fat, 152 mg Chol,
455 mg Sod, 19 g Carb, 2 g Sugar,
2 g Fib, 22 g Prot, 42 mg Calc.

# Stir-Fried Chicken and Vegetables with Crispy Ginger

SERVES 4

▲ ½ cup reduced-sodium chicken broth

2 tablespoons reduced-sodium soy sauce

2 tablespoons dry sherry

1 tablespoon cornstarch

1 tablespoon plus 1 teaspoon canola oil

2 (2-inch) pieces peeled fresh ginger, cut into thin strips

▲ ½ pound asparagus, trimmed and cut into 1½-inch pieces

▲ ½ pound sugar snap peas, trimmed

2 garlic cloves, crushed

2 tablespoons water

▲ 1 pound chicken tenders, cut lengthwise into ¼-inch slices

▲ 6 scallions, cut into 1½-inch pieces

PER SERVING (1 cup):
235 Cal, 8 g Total Fat, 1 g Sat Fat,
0 g Trans Fat, 63 mg Chol,
428 mg Sod, 13 g Carb, 4 g Sugar,
3 g Fib, 27 g Prot, 71 mg Calc.

1  Whisk together broth, soy sauce, sherry, and cornstarch in small bowl until smooth. Set aside.

2  To make crispy ginger, heat 1 tablespoon of oil in small saucepan over medium-high heat. Add ginger and cook, stirring constantly, until lightly browned, 2–3 minutes. With slotted spoon, transfer ginger to paper towel–lined plate.

3  Transfer remaining oil from saucepan to large heavy skillet or wok and heat over medium-high heat. Add asparagus, peas, and garlic; stir to coat vegetables with oil. Add water, reduce heat, and cook, covered, stirring occasionally, until vegetables are crisp-tender, 3–5 minutes. Transfer vegetables to large bowl.

4  Heat remaining 1 teaspoon oil in same skillet over medium-high heat. Add chicken and scallions; stir-fry until chicken is cooked through, about 4 minutes. Add vegetables and cornstarch mixture; cook, stirring constantly, until mixture comes to boil and sauce thickens, about 1 minute. Sprinkle with reserved crispy ginger and serve at once.

FYI  For even more green vegetables, you can stir 2 cups baby spinach into the stir-fry just before serving.

# Spicy Chicken and Broccoli Stir-Fry

SERVES 4

UNDER 20 MINUTES

▲ ¹/₂ cup reduced-sodium chicken broth

2 tablespoons dry sherry

1 tablespoon reduced-sodium soy sauce

1 tablespoon cornstarch

1¹/₂ teaspoons chili-garlic sauce

4 teaspoons canola oil

▲ 1 pound chicken tenders, cut lengthwise into ¹/₄-inch slices

▲ 4 cups small broccoli florets

▲ 2 small red or yellow bell peppers, thinly sliced

▲ 4 scallions, cut into ¹/₂-inch pieces

2 garlic cloves, minced

¹/₄ cup chopped fresh cilantro

PER SERVING (about 2 cups):
229 Cal, 8 g Total Fat, 1 g Sat Fat,
0 g Trans Fat, 63 mg Chol,
372 mg Sod, 12 g Carb, 2 g Sugar,
3 g Fib, 27 g Prot, 63 mg Calc.

1  Whisk together broth, sherry, soy sauce, cornstarch, and chili-garlic sauce in small bowl until smooth. Set aside.

2  Heat large heavy skillet or wok over medium-high heat until a drop of water sizzles in pan. Add 2 teaspoons of oil and swirl to coat skillet. Add chicken and cook, stirring often, until chicken is cooked through, about 4 minutes. Transfer to plate.

3  Add remaining 2 teaspoons oil to skillet. Add broccoli, bell peppers, and scallions and stir-fry until vegetables are crisp-tender, 3–5 minutes. Add garlic and stir-fry until fragrant, 30 seconds.

4  Add chicken and cornstarch mixture; cook, stirring constantly, until mixture comes to boil and sauce thickens, about 1 minute. Stir in cilantro and serve at once.

FYI  To soak up the spicy sauce, you can serve the stir-fry with brown rice (²/₃ cup cooked brown rice per serving will increase the *PointsPlus* value by *3).

# Apricot-Glazed Chicken with Crumb-Topped Tomatoes

SERVES 4

¼ cup apricot spreadable fruit

1 tablespoon balsamic vinegar

4 (5-ounce) skinless bone-in chicken thighs

2 teaspoons minced fresh rosemary

1 garlic clove, minced

½ teaspoon black pepper

¼ teaspoon salt

▲ 4 cups cherry tomatoes

3 tablespoons dried whole wheat bread crumbs

3 tablespoons grated Parmesan cheese

2 teaspoons olive oil

PER SERVING (1 chicken thigh with about 1 cup tomatoes):
295 Cal, 12 g Total Fat, 3 g Sat Fat, 0 g Trans Fat, 75 mg Chol, 359 mg Sod, 21 g Carb, 13 g Sugar, 2 g Fib, 23 g Prot, 89 mg Calc.

**7** PointsPlus® value

1  Spray broiler rack with nonstick spray and preheat broiler.

2  To make glaze, stir together spreadable fruit and vinegar in small bowl. Place chicken on broiler rack and sprinkle with rosemary, garlic, ¼ teaspoon of pepper, and salt. Broil 6 inches from heat for 5 minutes. Brush chicken with half of glaze. Broil, turning occasionally, and basting with remaining glaze, until chicken is cooked through, about 15 minutes longer. Cover to keep warm.

3  Spray another medium rimmed baking pan with non-stick spray. Place tomatoes in prepared pan. Broil 5 minutes. Stir together bread crumbs, Parmesan, oil, and remaining ¼ teaspoon pepper in small bowl. Sprinkle over tomatoes. Broil until crumbs are lightly browned, about 3 minutes longer. Serve chicken with tomatoes.

FYI  Steamed kale makes a healthful side dish for the chicken. To make it, trim and thinly slice 1 pound of kale and steam until tender, about 8 minutes. Drizzle with balsamic vinegar and sprinkle with salt and pepper to taste.

# Quick Chicken Carnitas

SERVES 4

2 teaspoons canola oil

▲ 1 pound chicken tenders, cut lengthwise into ¼-inch slices

▲ 1 onion, chopped

2 garlic cloves, minced

▲ 1 (14½-ounce) can diced tomatoes

2 teaspoons chili powder

1 teaspoon ground cumin

¼ teaspoon salt

¼ cup chopped fresh cilantro

8 (6-inch) corn tortillas, warmed

½ cup shredded reduced-fat Monterey Jack cheese

**PER SERVING (2 carnitas):**
366 Cal, 10 g Total Fat, 3 g Sat Fat, 0 g Trans Fat, 70 mg Chol, 775 mg Sod, 38 g Carb, 6 g Sugar, 4 g Fib, 30 g Prot, 248 mg Calc.

**9 PointsPlus© value**

1   Heat oil in large skillet over medium-high heat. Add chicken, onion, and garlic; cook, stirring, until chicken begins to brown, 8 minutes. Stir in tomatoes, chili powder, cumin, and salt. Reduce heat and simmer, stirring occasionally, about 10 minutes. Stir in cilantro.

2   Lay tortillas on work surface and spoon ¾ cup of chicken mixture down middle of each tortilla; sprinkle chicken evenly with cheese. Roll up to enclose filling. Serve at once.

**FYI** Carnitas are traditionally made with slow-simmered pork. This healthy chicken version is quick enough to make them a weeknight staple. Top each one with a spoonful of homemade Yellow Tomato Salsa: Combine 2 chopped yellow tomatoes, 2 each chopped green and red scallions, 1 teaspoon chopped jalapeno, zest and juice of 1 lime, and a touch of salt.

# Chicken and Vegetable Stir-Fry with Wasabi-Peanut Sauce

SERVES 6

▲ 1 cup brown rice

▲ 1 cup frozen green peas, thawed

³/₄ cup water

¹/₄ cup creamy peanut butter

1 tablespoon reduced-sodium soy sauce

1 teaspoon wasabi powder

4 (6-ounce) boneless skinless chicken thighs, cut in half crosswise

▲ 4 scallions, cut into 1-inch pieces

▲ 1 small green bell pepper, cut into 1-inch pieces

▲ 1 bunch radishes, thinly sliced

1 tablespoon peeled minced fresh ginger

3 garlic cloves, minced

PER SERVING (²/₃ cup chicken and vegetables with ¹/₂ cup rice):
307 Cal, 15 g Total Fat, 3 g Sat Fat,
0 g Trans Fat, 75 mg Chol,
173 mg Sod, 19 g Carb, 3 g Sugar,
3 g Fib, 26 g Prot, 42 mg Calc.

8 PointsPlus® value

1  Prepare rice according to package directions, omitting salt, if desired. Fluff rice with fork and stir in peas. Cover and keep warm.

2  Whisk together water, peanut butter, soy sauce, and wasabi in small bowl. Set aside.

3  Meanwhile, spray large heavy skillet or wok with nonstick spray and set over medium-high heat until drop of water sizzles in pan. Add chicken and cook, turning often, until browned and cooked through, about 10 minutes. Transfer to plate.

4  Spray same skillet with nonstick spray and set over medium heat. Add scallions, bell pepper, and radishes; stir-fry until vegetables are crisp-tender, about 3 minutes. Add ginger and garlic; stir-fry until fragrant, about 1 minute. Return chicken and any accumulated juices to skillet. Stir in reserved peanut butter mixture; increase heat and bring to boil. Reduce heat and simmer until sauce is slightly thickened, about 1 minute. Serve with rice mixture.

FYI  Stir-fry dishes require cooking over high heat. We find that cast-iron, heavy-bottomed stainless steel, or anodized steel skillets are the best for the task.

# Spicy Oven-Fried Drumsticks

¼ cup whole-wheat panko
bread crumbs

2 tablespoons all-purpose flour

1 teaspoon dried poultry
seasoning or sage

¾ teaspoon salt

½ teaspoon black pepper

½ teaspoon cayenne

¾ cup low-fat buttermilk

▲ 8 small skinless chicken
drumsticks (1¾ pounds)

**PER SERVING** (2 drumsticks):
203 Cal, 5 g Total Fat, 1 g Sat Fat,
0 g Trans Fat, 97 mg Chol,
595 mg Sod, 9 g Carb, 2 g Sugar,
1 g Fib, 28 g Prot, 73 mg Calc.

1  Preheat oven to 450°F. Line broiler pan with foil.

2  Mix together panko, flour, poultry seasoning, salt, pepper, and cayenne in large shallow bowl. Pour buttermilk into another bowl. Dip drumsticks, one at a time, into buttermilk mixture and roll in panko mixture to coat evenly.

3  Spray chicken lightly with nonstick spray and place in broiler pan. Bake until crispy and cooked through, about 25 minutes.

**FYI**  About 20 minutes before you bake the chicken, prick four sweet potatoes several times with the tip of a knife and place on a foil-lined baking sheet. Bake until tender, 40 to 45 minutes. One large sweet potato per serving will increase the **PointsPlus** value by **4.**

# Chicken Biryani

4 teaspoons canola oil

▲ 1 pound skinless boneless chicken breast, cut into ¹/₂-inch pieces

▲ 1 large onion, chopped

1 tablespoon minced peeled fresh ginger

2 garlic cloves, minced

1 teaspoon ground cumin

³/₄ teaspoon salt

¹/₂ teaspoon turmeric

¹/₄ teaspoon cinnamon

Pinch cayenne

▲ 1¹/₂ cups reduced-sodium chicken broth

1 cup basmati or long-grain white rice

¹/₄ cup chopped golden raisins

3 tablespoons slivered almonds, toasted

**PER SERVING (1¹/₂ cups):**
444 Cal, 11 g Total Fat, 2 g Sat Fat,
0 g Trans Fat, 63 mg Chol,
526 mg Sod, 55 g Carb, 9 g Sugar,
2 g Fib, 31 g Prot, 55 mg Calc.

**11**
PointsPlus®
value

1  Heat 2 teaspoons of oil in a large nonstick skillet over medium heat. Add chicken and cook, stirring often, until browned and cooked through, 3–4 minutes. Transfer to plate.

2  Add onion and cook, stirring frequently, until softened, 5 minutes. Add ginger, garlic, cumin, salt, turmeric, cinnamon, and cayenne, and cook, stirring constantly, until spices are fragrant, 1 minute. Add chicken, broth, rice, and raisins and bring to boil.

3  Reduce heat and simmer, covered, until rice is tender, about 20 minutes. Remove from heat and let rest 5 minutes. Spoon into large bowl and sprinkle with almonds.

**FYI**  Biryani is a rice-based dish popular in South Asia. You'll love this recipe not only because it's easy to make and delicious, but also because it cooks in one skillet.

# Creamy Chicken Paprikash with Fresh Dill

SERVES 4

UNDER 20 MINUTES

▲ 1 pound skinless boneless chicken breasts, cut into ½-inch pieces

½ teaspoon salt

⅛ teaspoon pepper

2 teaspoons olive oil

▲ 1 large onion, chopped

▲ 1 red bell pepper, seeded and thinly sliced

2 garlic cloves, minced

2 tablespoons paprika

2 tablespoons all-purpose flour

▲ 1 (14½-ounce) can diced tomatoes

▲ 1 cup reduced-sodium chicken broth

3 tablespoons light sour cream

3 tablespoons chopped fresh dill

PER SERVING (1¼ cups):
231 Cal, 7 g Total Fat, 2 g Sat Fat,
0 g Trans Fat, 66 mg Chol,
726 mg Sod, 16 g Carb, 7 g Sugar,
3 g Fib, 27 g Prot, 75 mg Calc.

1  Sprinkle chicken with salt and black pepper. Heat 1 teaspoon oil in large nonstick skillet over medium heat. Add chicken and cook, stirring often, until browned and cooked through, 3–4 minutes. Transfer to plate.

2  Add remaining 1 teaspoon oil to same skillet; add onion, bell pepper, and garlic. Cook, stirring frequently, until softened, 5 minutes. Add paprika and flour; cook, stirring constantly, 1 minute. Add tomatoes and broth and cook, stirring often, until mixture comes to boil and thickens slightly.

3  Return chicken to skillet and cook until heated through, 1 minute. Remove from heat; stir in sour cream and dill.

FYI  Whole wheat fettuccini is the perfect accompaniment to this saucy dish (½ cup of cooked whole wheat fettuccini will increase the *PointsPlus* value by *2*).

# Chicken Bolognese with Spaghetti Squash

SERVES 4

1 teaspoon olive oil

▲ 1 large carrot, chopped

▲ 1 large celery stalk, chopped

▲ 1 onion, chopped

2 garlic cloves, minced

▲ 1 pound ground skinless chicken breast

½ teaspoon black pepper

¼ teaspoon salt

¼ teaspoon ground nutmeg

½ cup dry white wine

▲ 1 (28-ounce) can plum tomatoes in puree, chopped

▲ 1 (4-pound) spaghetti squash, pricked several times with fork

▲ ¼ cup fat-free half-and-half

¼ cup coarsely chopped fresh parsley

**PER SERVING** (1½ cups squash with 1 cup sauce): 361 Cal, 5 g Total Fat, 1 g Sat Fat, 0 g Trans Fat, 63 mg Chol, 620 mg Sod, 43 g Carb, 21 g Sugar, 7 g Fib, 30 g Prot, 209 mg Calc.

1 To make sauce, heat oil in Dutch oven over medium heat. Add carrot, celery, and onion; cook, stirring occasionally, until vegetables are tender, 10–12 minutes. Add garlic and cook, stirring frequently, until fragrant, 30 seconds. Add chicken, pepper, salt, and nutmeg; increase heat and cook, breaking up chicken with wooden spoon, until chicken is no longer pink, about 5 minutes. Stir in wine and bring to boil. Stir in tomatoes and bring to boil. Reduce heat and simmer, stirring occasionally, until sauce is thickened, about 30 minutes.

2 Meanwhile, place squash in large microwavable dish. Microwave on High 8 minutes. Turn squash over. Microwave on High until fork-tender, 9–10 minutes. Let stand until cool enough to handle. Cut squash in half lengthwise and scoop out seeds. With fork, scrape out pulp and keep warm.

3 Stir half-and-half into sauce and cook until heated through, about 2 minutes. Remove from heat and stir in parsley. Serve sauce over squash.

**FYI** An easy accompaniment with this dish is a green salad of romaine, escarole, and endive tossed with balsamic vinegar and salt and pepper to taste.

# Open-Face Chicken Burgers with Tropical Salsa

SERVES 4

▲ 1 pound ground skinless chicken breast

▲ 2 scallions, minced

1/4 cup fresh whole wheat bread crumbs

▲ 2 tablespoons minced celery

▲ 2 tablespoons fat-free salsa

3/4 teaspoon ground cumin

1/2 teaspoon chili powder

▲ 1/2 peeled and cored fresh pineapple, chopped

▲ 2 kiwifruit, peeled and diced

▲ 1 scallion, sliced

1/4 cup chopped fresh cilantro

1 teaspoon grated lime zest

1 tablespoon lime juice

▲ 2 teaspoons diced pickled jalapeño peppers

2 whole wheat hamburger buns, split and toasted

▲ 4 lettuce leaves

**PER SERVING (1 open-face burger with 3/4 cup salsa):**
299 Cal, 5 g Total Fat, 1 g Sat Fat, 0 g Trans Fat, 63 mg Chol, 294 mg Sod, 38 g Carb, 18 g Sugar, 6 g Fib, 27 g Prot, 96 mg Calc.

1  Combine chicken, scallions, bread crumbs, celery, salsa, cumin, and chili powder in medium bowl and mix well. With damp hands, shape mixture into 4 (1/2-inch-thick) patties.

2  Spray large heavy skillet with nonstick spray and set over medium-high heat. Add patties and reduce heat to medium. Cook, partially covered, until instant-read thermometer inserted into side of each burger registers 165°F, 5–6 minutes on each side.

3  Meanwhile, to make salsa, stir together pineapple, kiwifruit, scallion, cilantro, lime zest and juice, and jalapeño in medium bowl.

4  Place buns, cut side up, on each of 4 serving plates. Top each bun half with 1 lettuce leaf and 1 burger. Top evenly with salsa.

**FYI** You can make fresh whole wheat crumbs by pulsing half of a whole wheat hamburger bun in a food processor.

# Chipotle-Roasted Drumsticks with Succotash Salsa

SERVES 4

▲ 2 scallions, chopped

1 chipotle en adobo plus
2 tablespoons adobo sauce

2 tablespoons tomato paste

2 tablespoons water

▲ 8 small skinless chicken
drumsticks (1³/₄ pounds)

▲ 1¹/₂ cups fresh corn kernels
(from 3 ears)

▲ 1 cup frozen baby lima
beans, thawed

▲ ¹/₂ cup grape tomatoes, halved

▲ ¹/₂ yellow bell pepper, thinly sliced

▲ ¹/₄ cup thinly sliced red onion

2 tablespoons chopped fresh cilantro

1 tablespoon lime juice

¹/₄ teaspoon salt

PER SERVING (2 drumsticks
with ²/₃ cup salsa):
282 Cal, 5 g Total Fat, 1 g Sat Fat,
0 g Trans Fat, 95 mg Chol,
517 mg Sod, 27 g Carb, 4 g Sugar,
5 g Fib, 32 g Prot, 49 mg Calc.

1  Preheat oven to 400°F. Line large rimmed baking pan with foil; spray foil with nonstick spray.

2  Combine scallions, chipotles en adobo, adobo sauce, tomato paste, and water in mini-food processor and process until scallions are finely chopped. Transfer mixture to large bowl; add chicken and toss to coat. Place chicken in single layer in baking pan. Roast until cooked through, 35–40 minutes.

3  Meanwhile, to make salsa, spray medium nonstick skillet with nonstick spray and set over medium heat. Add corn and cook, stirring occasionally, until lightly browned, 5–6 minutes. Transfer corn to bowl and let cool slightly, about 10 minutes. Add beans, tomatoes, bell pepper, onion, cilantro, lime juice, and salt and stir to mix well. Serve chicken with salsa.

FYI  The coating on the drumsticks is hot and spicy. If you prefer a less spicy dish, use only 1 tablespoon of the adobo sauce and increase tomato paste to 3 tablespoons.

CHIPOTLE-ROASTED DRUMSTICKS
WITH SUCCOTASH SALSA

# Greek Chicken and Spinach Phyllo Pie

SERVES 6

▲ 1 pound ground skinless
chicken breast

▲ 1 onion, chopped

1 garlic clove, minced

½ teaspoon curry powder

½ teaspoon ground cinnamon

¼ teaspoon ground allspice

¼ teaspoon salt

¼ teaspoon black pepper

▲ ½ cup tomato sauce

▲ 1 (10-ounce) package frozen
chopped spinach, thawed
and squeezed dry

1 cup crumbled reduced-fat
feta cheese

▲ 2 large egg whites, lightly beaten

8 (9 x 14-inch) sheets frozen
phyllo, thawed

**PER SERVING (1 wedge):**
239 Cal, 7 g Total Fat, 3 g Sat Fat,
0 g Trans Fat, 48 mg Chol,
730 mg Sod, 20 g Carb, 3 g Sugar,
3 g Fib, 25 g Prot, 153 mg Calc.

**1** Preheat oven to 375°F. Spray 9-inch pie plate with nonstick spray.

**2** To make filling, spray large nonstick skillet with nonstick spray and set over medium heat. Add chicken and onion; cook, breaking up chicken with wooden spoon, until chicken is no longer pink, about 8 minutes. Add garlic, curry powder, cinnamon, allspice, salt, and pepper; cook, stirring frequently, until fragrant, about 1 minute. Stir in tomato sauce and simmer until mixture is thickened, about 5 minutes. Transfer filling to large bowl. Stir in spinach and feta; stir in egg whites.

**3** Lay 1 phyllo sheet in pie plate; lightly spray with nonstick spray. Keep remaining phyllo covered with damp paper towel and plastic wrap to keep it from drying out. Repeat with 3 of the remaining phyllo sheets, placing corners at different angles and lightly spraying each sheet with nonstick spray. Spoon filling into crust.

**4** Top filling with remaining 4 phyllo sheets, repeating layering and spraying with nonstick spray. Roll up edges of phyllo toward center to form 1 ½-inch-wide rim.

**5** Bake until phyllo is golden brown, 30–35 minutes. Let stand 5 minutes before serving. Cut into 6 wedges.

**FYI** Yogurt sauce makes a great accompaniment to this traditional pie: To make a yogurt sauce, stir together ¾ cup plain fat-free yogurt, one half of an English (seedless) cucumber, chopped, 1 scallion, sliced, and ¼ teaspoon salt.

# Turkey Cutlets with Red Pepper and Prosciutto Sauce

SERVES 4

2 teaspoons olive oil

▲ 4 (4-ounce) turkey breast cutlets

▲ 2 onions, sliced

▲ 2 red bell peppers, thinly sliced

▲ 1 tomato, chopped

2 ounces prosciutto, diced

2 garlic cloves, finely chopped

▲ ½ cup low-sodium chicken broth

¼ cup dry white wine

¼ teaspoon salt

¼ teaspoon black pepper

2 tablespoons chopped fresh flat-leaf parsley

**PER SERVING (1 cutlet with ³/₄ cup vegetable mixture):**
237 Cal, 5 g Total Fat, 1 g Sat Fat, 0 g Trans Fat, 56 mg Chol, 637 mg Sod, 13 g Carb, 8 g Sugar, 3 g Fib, 34 g Prot, 35 mg Calc.

1   Heat 1 teaspoon of oil in large nonstick skillet over medium heat. Add turkey and cook until browned, 3–4 minutes on each side. Transfer to plate and set aside.

2   Add remaining 1 teaspoon oil to same skillet; add onions and bell peppers. Cook, stirring occasionally, until vegetables are very tender, 10 minutes. Add tomato, prosciutto, and garlic. Cook, stirring occasionally, until tomato is softened, about 6 minutes.

3   Add broth, wine, salt, and pepper to skillet; bring to boil. Reduce heat and simmer, covered, 10 minutes longer. Return turkey to skillet and cook until heated through, 2 minutes. Remove from heat and stir in parsley.

FYI   **You can serve this flavorful sauce with boneless skinless chicken breasts or with salmon fillets instead of the turkey if you wish.**

# Parmesan-Crusted Turkey with Arugula Salad

2 tablespoons whole wheat flour

▲ 1 large egg white

2 teaspoons water

3 tablespoons whole wheat panko bread crumbs

3 tablespoons grated Parmesan cheese

▲ 4 (4-ounce) turkey breast cutlets

1 teaspoon plus 1 tablespoon extra-virgin olive oil

1 tablespoon minced fresh chives

1 tablespoon red-wine vinegar

½ teaspoon Dijon mustard

¼ teaspoon black pepper

⅛ teaspoon salt

▲ 1 (5-ounce) container mixed baby greens or baby arugula

▲ 2 ripe green or plum tomatoes, cut into wedges

▲ ½ English (seedless) cucumber, coarsely chopped

¼ cup chopped pepperoncini or Tuscan peppers

**PER SERVING** (1 turkey cutlet with 1 cup salad):
243 Cal, 7 g Total Fat, 1 g Sat Fat, 0 g Trans Fat, 48 mg Chol, 446 mg Sod, 12 g Carb, 2 g Sugar, 3 g Fib, 34 g Prot, 112 mg Calc.

1 Place flour on sheet of wax paper. Beat together egg white and 1 teaspoon of water in shallow dish. Combine panko and Parmesan on another sheet of wax paper. Working with 1 cutlet at a time, dip both sides into flour. Dip into egg white mixture then into crumb mixture, pressing so it adheres.

2 Heat 1 teaspoon of oil in large nonstick skillet over medium heat. Add turkey and cook until golden brown and cooked through, 4–5 minutes on each side.

3 Meanwhile, whisk together remaining 1 tablespoon oil and 1 teaspoon water, chives, vinegar, mustard, pepper, and salt in large bowl. Add greens, tomatoes, cucumber, and pepperoncini; toss to coat. Serve turkey with salad.

FYI For additional crunch and spiciness, add 3 or 4 thinly sliced radishes to the salad.

# Turkey Scaloppini with Green Peppercorn and Mushroom Sauce

SERVES 4

▲ 4 ounces whole wheat angel hair pasta

▲ 1 (6-ounce) package fresh snow peas, thinly sliced diagonally

▲ 1 (1-pound) package thin-cut slices turkey breast for scaloppini

2 teaspoons olive oil

1 large shallot, minced

▲ 1 (4-ounce) package sliced mixed mushrooms

▲ ³/₄ cup reduced-sodium chicken broth

¹/₄ cup dry white wine

1 tablespoon green peppercorns in brine, rinsed and drained

2 teaspoons Dijon mustard

¹/₄ teaspoon salt

PER SERVING (3 pieces turkey, 1 cup pasta, and ¹/₄ cup sauce): 302 Cal, 4 g Total Fat, 0 g Sat Fat, 0 g Trans Fat, 45 mg Chol, 379 mg Sod, 29 g Carb, 4 g Sugar, 4 g Fib, 35 g Prot, 42 mg Calc.

1  Cook pasta according to package directions, omitting salt, if desired, and adding peas during last 1 minute of cooking time. Drain and keep warm.

2  Meanwhile, cut each turkey slice crosswise in half to make a total of 12 pieces. Spray large nonstick skillet with nonstick spray and set over medium heat. Add turkey and cook, turning once, until lightly browned and cooked through, 5–6 minutes. Transfer turkey to plate.

3  Heat oil in same skillet over medium heat. Add shallot and cook, stirring frequently, until softened, about 2 minutes. Add mushrooms and cook, stirring occasionally, until lightly browned, about 5 minutes. Stir in broth, wine, peppercorns, mustard, and salt; increase heat and bring to boil. Boil 1 minute. Return turkey to skillet and cook until heated through, about 2 minutes. Serve turkey and mushroom sauce with pasta.

FYI  Green peppercorns are immature black peppercorns. They are tender and milder in flavor than black peppercorns and are used in many dishes for their bright, pungent flavor.

# Southwest Turkey Burgers

SERVES 4

UNDER 20 MINUTES

▲ **1 pound ground skinless turkey breast**

▲ **1 large egg**

**3 tablespoons dried bread crumbs**

**1 jalapeño, seeded and minced**

**1 small garlic clove, minced**

**1 teaspoon ground cumin**

**½ teaspoon chili powder**

**½ teaspoon salt**

**4 whole wheat hamburger buns**

▲ **4 leaf lettuce leaves**

▲ **½ cup prepared fat-free salsa**

PER SERVING (1 burger):
290 Cal, 5 g Total Fat, 1 g Sat Fat,
0 g Trans Fat, 99 mg Chol,
739 mg Sod, 29 g Carb, 5 g Sugar,
4 g Fib, 34 g Prot, 68 mg Calc.

1  Combine turkey, egg, bread crumbs, jalapeño, garlic, cumin, chili powder, and salt in a medium bowl. With damp hands, form mixture into 4 (½-inch-thick) patties.

2  Spray medium nonstick skillet with nonstick spray and set over medium heat. Add patties and cook until instant-read thermometer inserted in side of each burger registers 165°F, 6–8 minutes on each side.

3  Place burgers in buns with lettuce leaves and salsa.

**FYI**  You can serve the burgers with baby carrots and red bell pepper strips for a healthful and filling lunch.

# Turkey, Zucchini, and Quinoa Meatloaves

SERVES 6

▲ ½ cup quinoa, rinsed

▲ 1 zucchini, coarsely shredded

▲ 2 large egg whites

½ cup chili sauce

▲ ½ onion, finely chopped

1 tablespoon chopped fresh sage

½ teaspoon salt

½ teaspoon black pepper

▲ 1 pound ground skinless turkey breast

1 tablespoon spicy brown mustard

**PER SERVING (1 meat loaf):**
195 Cal, 4 g Total Fat, 1 g Sat Fat,
0 g Trans Fat, 102 mg Chol,
595 mg Sod, 18 g Carb, 5 g Sugar,
2 g Fib, 23 g Prot, 24 mg Calc.

1 Cook quinoa according to package directions. Fluff with fork and let cool slightly.

2 Preheat to 425°F. Line large rimmed baking pan with foil; spray foil with nonstick spray.

3 Squeeze zucchini dry and place in large bowl with egg whites, ¼ cup of chili sauce, onion, sage, salt, and pepper. Add turkey and quinoa and stir to mix well.

4 Shape into 6 (2 ½ x 4-inch) oval loaves. Place loaves on baking pan. Stir together remaining ¼ cup chili sauce and mustard in small bowl; spread mixture evenly over loaves.

5 Bake until instant-read thermometer inserted into side of each loaf registers 165°F, 30–35 minutes. Let stand 5 minutes before serving.

TURKEY, ZUCCHINI, AND
QUINOA MEATLOAVES

# Seafood

## Main Dishes

# Seafood

**YOU NEED**

1 to 2 servings per day of lean protein; 2 to 3 ounces of cooked seafood counts as 1 serving.

**WHY THEY'RE ESSENTIAL**

**Eat your Omega-3s.** Fish such as wild salmon and trout, and water-packed canned salmon, tuna, and mackerel are excellent sources of omega-3 fatty acids, which may help improve your mood and reduce inflammation that is associated with developing heart disease.

**Fish is heart-smart.** It's low in saturated fat and the nutrients in fish may decrease your risk of having an irregular heartbeat, decrease triglyceride levels, and slow the growth of plaque that can lead to a heart attack.

**Get plenty of minerals.** Seafood is one of the best sources of minerals. From calcium in the small soft bones of canned fish to zinc and iron in oysters, to iodine, phosphorous, and selenium in all types of seafood, fish and shellfish are an excellent source of these vital nutrients.

**Seafood is skinny.** Most fish and shellfish are very low in fat and are an excellent source of protein. Salmon is higher in fat than other fish, but the fat it contains is the heart-healthy kind.

**WHAT TO BUY**

**Fish:** For sustainability, line-caught albacore tuna from the United States or British Columbia, and wild Alaska salmon and coho salmon; rainbow trout, Arctic char, and barramundi farmed in the U.S. in tank systems are among the best choices.

*TIP: Frozen fish fillets are an economical option; they thaw quickly and are convenient to have on hand for quick dinners.*

**Shellfish:** Farmed or wild-caught oysters, clams, and scallops; farmed mussels; and wild-caught or U.S. farmed shrimp are excellent shellfish choices.

*TIP: Avoid imported shrimp—most are farmed in open systems that harm the environment.*

**Canned water-packed tuna and salmon:** Look for "light" tuna, which comes from a smaller variety of tuna and is more abundant than the larger yellow fin and skipjack. It also contains less mercury than larger tuna. Always buy wild Alaska canned salmon.

*TIP: Buying skinned boneless canned salmon is a little more expensive, but it's a time-saver.*

**GOOD TO KNOW**

**Watch out for mercury.** Mercury found in large predatory fish, such as tuna, swordfish, and shark, can be detrimental to the nervous system of women of childbearing age and young children. The FDA recommends these groups should eat less than 12 ounces of these fish per week. For others, the heart-health benefits outweigh the risks.

**Be sustainable.** Help the oceans, the environment, and your health by buying seafood that is sustainably caught or raised in an environmentally friendly manner. Go to www.montereybay-aquarium.org to download a list of the best seafood choices for your region of the country. Look for a blue MSC (Marine Stewardship Council) sticker on fresh, frozen, and canned seafood. It has the approval of the MSC certifying that it is caught or raised in a sustainable, environmentally friendly way.

## Fish

### POWER-UP IDEAS

- Grilled fish is a healthy alternative to steaks or burgers. Grill it with the skin on to keep it intact while cooking, but remove it before eating.

- Steam quick-cooking vegetables such as sliced bell peppers, zucchini, or broccoli along with fish fillets for a quick one-pan meal.

- Most fish fillets cook in less than 10 minutes, so there's no excuse not to have a healthy dinner.

### TAKE NOTE

- Keep your healthy choice healthy—always bake, broil, or grill fish.

- Plain fish fillets are low in sodium; avoid premarinated or prebreaded versions, which may be high in sodium.

- Cooked seafood is always safest, but if you do choose to eat it raw, eating seafood that has been previously frozen is slightly safer. Freezing will kill parasites, but not all the harmful bacteria.

## Shellfish

### POWER-UP IDEAS

- Shrimp and scallops are a natural for stir-fries. They cook quickly and require little prep before cooking.

- Steam mussels or clams with white wine, lemon juice, and garlic. Serve over whole wheat pasta for a simple dinner.

- Use precooked shrimp from the deli to add to pasta salads or green salads or chop them and turn into a shrimp salad.

### TAKE NOTE

- Cholesterol levels in shrimp are from 1 to $1\frac{1}{2}$ times higher than in dark meat chicken, but shrimp have less cholesterol than eggs.

- USDA Dietary Guidelines recommend at least two servings of seafood each week. Shrimp and scallops make it easy to meet the advice: They're almost universally enjoyed and they're quick and easy to cook.

## Canned water-packed tuna and salmon

### POWER-UP IDEAS

- Skip the mayo: Combine canned tuna or salmon, lemon zest and juice, and minced celery and onion for a healthful seafood salad.

- Top a green salad with canned tuna or salmon for a quick protein-rich lunch.

- Turn your favorite fish cakes recipe into fish burgers: Shape the cakes into flat burgers, cook in a nonstick skillet and serve on whole wheat buns with lettuce and tomato.

### TAKE NOTE

- We have to eat omega-3s— our bodies don't make them, and canned fish is one of the easiest and most delicious ways to get these vital nutrients.

- Not familiar with canned salmon? Use it the same way you do canned tuna: in salads, sandwiches, or fish cakes.

- Canned sockeye salmon has slightly more omega-3s than pink salmon.

# Grilled Arctic Char and Watercress Salad with Mustard-Mint Sauce

SERVES 4

UNDER 20 MINUTES

½ cup chopped fresh mint

4 teaspoons Dijon mustard

1½ teaspoons honey

1 teaspoon prepared horseradish sauce

1 teaspoon water

▲ 4 (6-ounce) Arctic char fillets

¼ teaspoon salt

¼ teaspoon black pepper

1 tablespoon sherry vinegar

1½ teaspoons olive oil

▲ 2 bunches watercress, trimmed

▲ ½ small red onion, thinly sliced

PER SERVING (1 Arctic char fillet, 1¼ cups salad, and 2 teaspoons sauce):
219 Cal, 10 g Total Fat, 2 g Sat Fat,
0 g Trans Fat, 62 mg Chol,
378 mg Sod, 5 g Carb, 3 g Sugar,
1 g Fib, 28 g Prot, 80 mg Calc.

**1** To make sauce, stir together mint, mustard, honey, horseradish, and water in small bowl. Set aside.

**2** Spray ridged grill pan with nonstick spray; set over medium heat until hot. Sprinkle arctic char with ⅛ teaspoon salt and ⅛ teaspoon pepper. Place in grill pan and cook until lightly browned and just opaque in center, 4–5 minutes on each side.

**3** Meanwhile, whisk together vinegar, oil, remaining ⅛ teaspoon salt and ⅛ teaspoon pepper in large bowl. Add watercress and onion and toss to coat. Top watercress with salmon. Drizzle salmon evenly with sauce.

**FYI** Arctic char is a member of the trout and salmon family. It's available both wild and farm raised and is a smarter ecological choice than most farm-raised salmon. Wild char is available only for a short time in the fall, but farm-raised char is available year-round. It's farmed in land-based farms in an ecologically responsible manner.

# Salmon Panzanella with Fresh Basil

SERVES 4

UNDER 20 MINUTES

1 teaspoon grated lemon zest

2 tablespoons lemon juice

1 tablespoon red-wine vinegar

2 teaspoons olive oil

¼ teaspoon salt

¼ teaspoon black pepper

▲ 4 medium tomatoes, cut into ¾-inch chunks

▲ ½ cup roasted red peppers, drained and coarsely chopped (not oil packed)

▲ ½ small red onion, thinly sliced

8 kalamata olives, pitted and chopped

▲ 1 (14 ¾-ounce) can water-packed wild Alaskan salmon, drained

▲ 1 small English (seedless) cucumber, quartered lengthwise and sliced

4 (¾-inch-thick) slices whole wheat ciabatta bread, toasted and cut into cubes

1½ cups fresh basil leaves, torn

**PER SERVING (2 cups):**
346 Cal, 12 g Total Fat, 2 g Sat Fat, 0 g Trans Fat, 72 mg Chol, 937 mg Sod, 25 g Carb, 7 g Sugar, 5 g Fib, 34 g Prot, 105 mg Calc.

**1** Whisk together lemon zest and juice, vinegar, oil, salt, and pepper in large bowl. Stir in tomatoes, peppers, onion, and olives; let stand 10 minutes.

**2** Meanwhile, remove skin and bones from salmon and discard; break salmon into large chunks. Gently stir salmon, cucumber, and bread into tomato mixture. Let stand until bread soaks up some of the juices, about 5 minutes. Stir in basil and serve at once.

**FYI** To make this a more filling meal, serve the panzanella on a bed of mixed greens or baby spinach.

# Broiled Tuna Steaks with Pesto and Greens

SERVES 4

UNDER 20 MINUTES

1½ cups lightly packed fresh basil leaves

▲ 3 tablespoons reduced-sodium chicken broth

3 tablespoons grated Parmesan cheese

1 tablespoon slivered almonds

1 garlic clove, chopped

2 teaspoons lemon juice

1 teaspoon extra-virgin olive oil

⅛ teaspoon salt

▲ 4 (5-ounce) tuna steaks

▲ 1 bunch red dandelion greens

½ cup water

PER SERVING (1 tuna steak, ¾ cup spinach, and 1 tablespoon pesto): 274 Cal, 11 g Total Fat, 3 g Sat Fat, 0 g Trans Fat, 59 mg Chol, 243 mg Sod, 5 g Carb, 1 g Sugar, 3 g Fib, 39 g Prot, 178 mg Calc.

7 PointsPlus© value

**1**  To make pesto, combine basil, broth, cheese, almonds, garlic, lemon juice, oil, and salt in a blender or food processor and process until smooth. Place tuna on large plate and spread both sides with 3 tablespoons pesto. Let stand at room temperature for 10 minutes.

**2**  Spray broiler rack with nonstick spray; preheat broiler. Place tuna on broiler rack and broil 5 inches from heat, 1–2 minutes on each side for medium.

**3**  Meanwhile, combine greens and water in large saucepan; bring to boil over medium-high heat. Reduce heat and simmer until greens are tender, 10–12 minutes. Drain greens and divide among 4 plates. Top greens with tuna. Top tuna evenly with remaining pesto.

**FYI**  To make a side dish for the tuna, you can cut 8 small potatoes in half and steam them. Sprinkle with salt and pepper to taste. Two small potatoes will increase the per-serving *PointsPlus* value by **6**. You can serve the tuna with steamed spinach if fresh red dandelion greens are not available.

# Tuna with Fennel, Oranges, and Mint

SERVES 4

▲ 1 large fennel bulb, trimmed and sliced

▲ 4 (5-ounce) tuna steaks

¼ teaspoon salt

▲ 2 navel oranges, peeled and cut into segments

½ cup fresh mint leaves, torn

2 tablespoons red-wine vinegar

2 teaspoons extra-virgin olive oil

⅛ teaspoon red pepper flakes

2 tablespoons sliced almonds, toasted

**PER SERVING (1 tuna steak with ¾ cup salad):**
301 Cal, 11 g Total Fat, 2 g Sat Fat, 0 g Trans Fat, 56 mg Chol, 235 mg Sod, 14 g Carb, 6 g Sugar, 4 g Fib, 36 g Prot, 86 mg Calc.

**1** Spray ridged grill pan with nonstick spray and set over medium heat until hot. Add fennel and cook, turning occasionally, until tender and lightly browned, about 8 minutes. Transfer fennel to cutting board.

**2** Sprinkle tuna with ⅛ teaspoon salt. Spray same grill pan with nonstick spray. Place tuna on grill pan and cook 1–2 minutes on each side for medium.

**3** Meanwhile, coarsely chop fennel. Stir together fennel, oranges, mint, vinegar, oil, red pepper flakes, and remaining ⅛ teaspoon salt in large bowl. Top tuna evenly with fennel mixture and sprinkle with almonds. Serve at once.

**FYI** To add more fruit to the salad, stir in a red grapefruit, peeled and cut into segments.

# Catfish and Vegetable Stir-Fry

SERVES 4

UNDER 20 MINUTES

▲ 1 pound catfish fillets, cut into 1-inch chunks

1 tablespoon rice vinegar

2 teaspoons canola oil

3 garlic cloves, minced

1 tablespoon minced peeled fresh ginger

▲ ½ small head Savoy cabbage, thinly sliced (about 5 cups)

▲ 3 cups broccoli florets

▲ 2 carrots, thinly sliced diagonally

▲ 1 red bell pepper, thinly sliced

▲ ¾ cup reduced-sodium chicken broth

2 tablespoons reduced-sodium soy sauce

▲ 3 scallions, thinly sliced

▲ 2 cups hot cooked brown rice

PER SERVING (2¼ cups fish and vegetables with ½ cup rice):
341 Cal, 10 g Total Fat, 3 g Sat Fat,
0 g Trans Fat, 51 mg Chol,
385 mg Sod, 39 g Carb, 5 g Sugar,
8 g Fib, 25 g Prot, 94 mg Calc.

**1** Place catfish and vinegar in medium bowl and toss to coat. Set aside.

**2** Set large heavy skillet or wok over medium-high heat until drop of water sizzles in pan. Add oil and swirl to coat pan. Add garlic and ginger and cook, stirring constantly, until fragrant, 30 seconds. Add cabbage, broccoli, carrots, and bell pepper; stir-fry until vegetables begin to soften, 2 minutes.

**3** Add broth and soy sauce and bring to boil. Add catfish; cover and cook, stirring occasionally, until catfish is just opaque throughout, 2–3 minutes. Remove from heat and stir in scallions. Serve over rice.

**FYI** Tilapia is a good substitute for catfish because it's firm enough not to break apart in the stir-fry. When buying catfish or tilapia, look for fish that's farmed in the United States, where more ecologically friendly farming methods are used.

Seafood

# Cod with Roasted Tomatoes and Green Olives

SERVES 4

▲ 4 plum tomatoes, cut into wedges

2 tablespoons balsamic vinegar

2 teaspoons fresh thyme leaves

1 teaspoon olive oil

▲ 1 large sweet onion, sliced

▲ 1 yellow bell pepper, chopped

3 garlic cloves, minced

¼ cup pimiento-stuffed green olives, chopped

▲ 4 (5-ounce) cod fillets

⅛ teaspoon black pepper

⅛ teaspoon salt

PER SERVING (1 fillet with ¾ cup sauce):
196 Cal, 5 g Total Fat, 1 g Sat Fat,
0 g Trans Fat, 54 mg Chol,
382 mg Sod, 14 g Carb, 8 g Sugar,
3 g Fib, 24 g Prot, 57 mg Calc.

**1** Preheat oven to 450°F. Spray 9 x 13-inch baking dish with nonstick spray. Arrange tomatoes, cut sides up, in prepared dish. Drizzle with 1 tablespoon vinegar and sprinkle with thyme. Roast until tomatoes are soft, turning once, about 12 minutes.

**2** Meanwhile, heat oil in large nonstick skillet over medium-high heat. Add onion and cook, stirring frequently, until lightly browned, about 4 minutes. Reduce heat to medium and stir in bell pepper and garlic. Cook, stirring frequently, until pepper is soft, about 8 minutes.

**3** Add onion mixture and olives to tomato mixture. Place fish fillets on top of vegetable mixture. Drizzle fish with remaining 1 tablespoon vinegar. Sprinkle with salt and pepper. Bake until fish is just opaque in center, about 12 minutes. If cod has skin still on it, remove it before eating.

**FYI** Pacific cod from Alaska is the most sustainable choice since those caught in the Pacific are line or trap-caught. Atlantic cod and imported cod are caught mainly by trawling, which can damage the seafloor and destroy fish habitats. Serve the cod with steamed green beans to round out the meal.

# Broiled Cod with White Bean, Roasted Pepper, and Olive Salad

SERVES 4

▲ 1 (15½-ounce) can cannellini (white kidney) beans, rinsed and drained

▲ 1 cup chopped roasted red peppers (not oil packed)

▲ ½ small red onion, chopped

½ cup chopped fresh flat-leaf parsley

¼ cup kalamata olives, pitted and chopped

1 tablespoon finely crumbled feta cheese

1½ teaspoons olive oil

¼ teaspoon salt

¼ teaspoon black pepper

▲ 4 (5-ounce) cod fillets

Lemon wedges

PER SERVING (1 fish fillet with ¾ cup salad): 254 Cal, 5 g Total Fat, 1 g Sat Fat, 0 g Trans Fat, 56 mg Chol, 904 mg Sod, 21 g Carb, 3 g Sugar, 6 g Fib, 30 g Prot, 95 mg Calc

**1**  To make salad, stir together beans, peppers, onion, parsley, olives, cheese, oil, ⅛ teaspoon salt, and ⅛ teaspoon pepper in large bowl.

**2**  Spray broiler rack with nonstick spray; preheat broiler. Sprinkle cod with remaining ⅛ teaspoon salt and ⅛ teaspoon pepper. Place cod on broiler rack and broil 5 inches from heat until cod is just opaque throughout, about 7 minutes. Serve cod with salad and lemon wedges.

**FYI**  You can make this salad more colorful and filling by adding 1 cup of halved cherry tomatoes.

# Steamed Sole and Vegetables with Black Bean Sauce

SERVES 4

UNDER 20 MINUTES

▲ 4 (5-ounce) sole fillets

1½ teaspoons Asian (dark) sesame oil

▲ 2 scallions, chopped

▲ 1 (1 pound) bag frozen stir-fry vegetables

1 cup water

▲ ⅓ cup reduced-sodium chicken broth

2 tablespoons rice vinegar

1 tablespoon low-sodium soy sauce

2 teaspoons black bean sauce

2 teaspoons minced peeled fresh ginger

1 garlic clove, minced

1 teaspoon cornstarch

PER SERVING (1 fish fillet, ¾ cup vegetables, and scant 2 tablespoons sauce): 186 Cal, 4 g Total Fat, 1 g Sat Fat, 0 g Trans Fat, 67 mg Chol, 284 mg Sod, 9 g Carb, 3 g Sugar, 2 g Fib, 26 g Prot, 55 mg Calc.

**1** Spray bottom of steamer basket with nonstick spray. Brush sole with 1 teaspoon sesame oil, sprinkle one side with scallions, and fold each fillet in half lengthwise. Place in steamer basket; set in skillet over 1 inch boiling water. Cover and steam until fish is just opaque throughout, 6–8 minutes.

**2** Meanwhile combine stir-fry vegetables and water in 10-inch skillet, spreading vegetables to an even layer. Set over medium-high heat and bring to boil. Reduce heat, cover, and cook until vegetables are crisp-tender, about 5 minutes.

**3** Whisk together broth, vinegar, soy sauce, black bean sauce, ginger, garlic, cornstarch, and remaining ½ teaspoon sesame oil in small saucepan until smooth. Set over medium-high heat and cook, stirring often, until mixture comes to boil and thickens, about 2 minutes.

**4** Place 1 sole fillet on each of 4 serving plates. Drain vegetables and divide evenly among plates. Drizzle sauce evenly over sole and vegetables.

**FYI** To complete the meal, serve the fish and vegetables with brown rice (⅔ cup cooked brown rice for each serving will increase the *PointsPlus* value by *3*).

Seafood

# Vegetable Stuffed Sole with Dill Butter

SERVES 4

▲ 1 large carrot, cut into matchstick strips

▲ ½ red bell pepper, cut into matchstick strips

▲ 1 zucchini, cut into matchstick strips

2 tablespoons water

▲ 4 (5-ounce) sole fillets, each halved lengthwise

¼ teaspoon salt

4 teaspoons unsalted butter, softened

1½ tablespoons chopped fresh dill

1 teaspoon grated lemon zest

¼ teaspoon fennel seeds, crushed

Lemon wedges

PER SERVING (2 rolled fillets):
170 Cal, 6 g Total Fat, 3 g Sat Fat,
0 g Trans Fat, 77 mg Chol,
267 mg Sod, 4 g Carb, 2 g Sugar,
1 g Fib, 25 g Prot, 36 mg Calc.

**1** Preheat oven to 400°F. Spray 9 x 13-inch baking dish with nonstick spray.

**2** Combine carrot, bell pepper, zucchini, and water in medium microwavable dish. Cover and microwave on High until crisp-tender, about 3 minutes. Drain and let stand until cool enough to handle.

**3** Place sole fillets, skinned side up, on work surface and sprinkle with salt. Place about ½ cup of vegetable mixture at wide end of each fillet. Roll up jelly-roll style and place seam side down in baking dish. Cover dish with foil and bake until sole is just opaque in center, 12–15 minutes.

**4** Meanwhile, stir together butter, dill, lemon zest, and fennel seeds in small bowl. Spread fish fillets evenly with butter mixture. Serve with lemon wedges.

**FYI** You can use flounder instead of sole for this recipe.

**VEGETABLE STUFFED SOLE
WITH DILL BUTTER**

3 tablespoons lime juice

1 tablespoon canola oil

1 tablespoon Asian fish sauce

1 teaspoon grated peeled fresh ginger

1 teaspoon sugar

1 garlic clove, minced

1/8 teaspoon red pepper flakes

▲ 2 medium carrots, cut into matchstick strips

▲ 4 (5-ounce) striped bass fillets

▲ 4 ounces snow peas, cut into matchstick strips

▲ 1 scallion, thinly sliced

1/4 cup chopped fresh cilantro

**PER SERVING (1 packet):**
206 Cal, 7 g Total Fat, 1 g Sat Fat,
0 g Trans Fat, 117 mg Chol,
470 mg Sod, 8 g Carb, 4 g Sugar,
2 g Fib, 27 g Prot, 52 mg Calc.

# Grilled Thai Fish and Vegetable Packets

**1**  Preheat grill to medium or prepare medium fire.

**2**  Whisk together lime juice, oil, fish sauce, ginger, sugar, garlic, and pepper flakes in small bowl.

**3**  Tear off 4 (18-inch) sheets of foil. Arrange carrots evenly in center of each sheet; top carrots with fish fillets. Drizzle fish evenly with lime juice mixture. Sprinkle each fillet evenly with peas and scallion. Fold each piece of foil into a packet, making a tight seal and allowing room for packets to expand.

**4**  Place packets on grill rack and grill, covered, until fish is just opaque in center, about 8 minutes. Open packets carefully when testing for doneness, as steam will escape. Transfer fish, vegetables, and accumulated cooking juices to serving plates. Sprinkle evenly with cilantro.

**FYI**  If you have zucchini on hand, cut one into thin slices and arrange it evenly in the bottom of the packets along with the carrots.

# Curried Tilapia and Vegetables with Yogurt-Mint Sauce

SERVES 4

▲ 1 onion, chopped

▲ 1 large red bell pepper, chopped

▲ 2 celery stalks, thinly sliced

3 garlic cloves, minced

1 teaspoon curry powder

▲ 1 cup reduced-sodium chicken broth

▲ 1 large Granny Smith apple, peeled, cored, and cut into ³⁄₄-inch chunks

▲ 4 (5-ounce) tilapia fillets

¹⁄₄ teaspoon salt

¹⁄₈ teaspoon black pepper

▲ ¹⁄₄ cup fat-free Greek yogurt

2 tablespoons chopped fresh mint

PER SERVING (1 fish fillet, about ³⁄₄ cup vegetable mixture, and 1 tablespoon yogurt): 203 Cal, 4 g Total Fat, 1 g Sat Fat, 0 g Trans Fat, 61 mg Chol, 261 mg Sod, 13 g Carb, 8 g Sugar, 3 g Fib, 31 g Prot, 60 mg Calc.

**1**  Spray large skillet with nonstick spray and set over medium heat. Add onion, bell pepper, and celery and cook, stirring frequently, until vegetables soften, about 6 minutes. Stir in garlic and ³⁄₄ teaspoon of curry powder and cook, stirring constantly, until fragrant, 30 seconds. Stir in broth and apple.

**2**  Sprinkle tilapia with remaining ¹⁄₄ teaspoon curry powder, salt, and pepper. Arrange tilapia fillets in single layer over vegetables; bring to boil. Reduce heat and simmer, covered, until tilapia is just opaque throughout, 6–7 minutes.

**3**  Meanwhile, stir together yogurt and mint in small bowl. Transfer tilapia and vegetables to serving plates. Top tilapia evenly with yogurt mixture.

**FYI**  You can add ¹⁄₂ pound green beans, cut into 1-inch pieces, along with the apple in this dish. If you do so, increase the broth to 1¹⁄₂ cups.

Seafood

# Seafood and White Bean Chowder

SERVES 4

2 teaspoons olive oil

▲ 2 carrots, chopped

▲ 2 celery stalks, chopped

▲ 1 large onion, chopped

▲ 2 cups reduced-sodium chicken broth

▲ 1 pound red potatoes, cut into ¾-inch chunks

½ teaspoon dried thyme

¼ teaspoon black pepper

▲ 2 (6½-ounce) cans chopped clams

▲ 1 (15½-ounce) can no-salt-added cannellini (white kidney) beans, rinsed and drained

▲ ¾ pound cod fillet, cut into 1-inch chunks

▲ 1 cup fresh or frozen corn kernels

▲ ¾ cup fat-free half-and-half

2 tablespoons chopped fresh flat-leaf parsley

PER SERVING (2 cups): 360 Cal, 4 g Total Fat, 1 g Sat Fat, 0 g Trans Fat, 35 mg Chol, 395 mg Sod, 54 g Carb, 10 g Sugar, 13 g Fib, 28 g Prot, 173 mg Calc.

**1** Heat oil in Dutch oven over medium heat. Add carrots, celery, and onion and cook, stirring occasionally, until vegetables are softened, about 6 minutes. Add broth, potatoes, thyme, and pepper and bring to boil. Reduce heat, cover, and simmer 5 minutes.

**2** Stir in clams and their juice and beans and return to boil. Reduce heat; cover and simmer until potatoes are tender, about 10 minutes. Stir in cod and corn; cover and simmer until cod is just opaque throughout, 4–5 minutes. With back of spoon, mash some of potatoes against side of pot. Stir in half-and-half and parsley. Remove from heat and let stand, covered, 1 minute.

**FYI** To use fresh shellfish instead of the canned clams, add 1 pound small clams or mussels, or a combination of both, when you add the cod. Cook until the shells open, about 5 minutes. Discard any shells that don't open.

SEAFOOD AND WHITE
BEAN CHOWDER

# Spaghetti with Sardines, Broccoli, and Cauliflower

SERVES 4

▲ 6 ounces whole-wheat spaghetti

▲ 1 (1-pound) package frozen broccoli and cauliflower blend, thawed

1 tablespoon olive oil

▲ 1 large onion, chopped

3 garlic cloves, minced

1/4 teaspoon red pepper flakes

1/4 teaspoon salt

1/3 cup golden raisins

1/4 teaspoon saffron threads, crumbled (optional)

2 (3 3/4-ounce) cans no-salt-added sardines in water, drained

4 tablespoons grated Pecorino Romano or Parmesan cheese

PER SERVING (1 3/4 cups):
344 Cal, 6 g Total Fat, 2 g Sat Fat,
0 g Trans Fat, 62 mg Chol,
376 mg Sod, 52 g Carb, 14 g Sugar,
9 g Fib, 22 g Prot, 239 mg Calc.

**1** Cook spaghetti according to package directions, omitting salt, if desired, and adding broccoli and cauliflower during last 5 minutes of cooking time. Drain pasta and vegetables, reserving 3/4 cup of the cooking liquid.

**2** Meanwhile, heat oil in large deep skillet over medium-low heat. Add onion and cook, stirring occasionally, until golden brown, about 12 minutes. Add garlic, pepper flakes, and salt; cook, stirring constantly, 1 minute. Stir in raisins, saffron (if using), and 1/2 cup reserved cooking liquid; simmer 3 minutes.

**3** Remove and discard backbones from sardines and break into chunks. Add pasta mixture and sardines to onion mixture and cook, stirring constantly, just until heated through, 1–2 minutes, adding remaining 1/4 cup cooking liquid if mixture seems dry. Divide pasta mixture among 4 serving plates and sprinkle each serving with 1 tablespoon of cheese.

**FYI** You can substitute 2 (5-ounce) cans chunk light tuna in water, drained, for the sardines.

# Peruvian Seafood Stew

2 teaspoons olive oil

▲ 1 large onion, chopped

3 garlic cloves, minced

▲ 1 jalapeño pepper, seeded and minced

1½ cups water

1 (8-ounce) bottle clam juice

▲ ¾ pound small red potatoes, thinly sliced

¼ teaspoon salt

▲ ¾ pound cod fillets, cut into 1-inch chunks

▲ ½ pound medium shrimp, peeled and deveined

¼ cup chopped fresh cilantro

Lime wedges

**PER SERVING** (1½ cups):
204 Cal, 4 g Total Fat, 1 g Sat Fat,
0 g Trans Fat, 118 mg Chol,
420 mg Sod, 18 g Carb, 3 g Sugar,
2 g Fib, 25 g Prot, 57 mg Calc.

**1** Heat oil in Dutch oven over medium heat. Add onion and cook, stirring occasionally, until onion begins to brown, about 7 minutes. Add garlic and jalapeño and cook, stirring constantly, 1 minute. Add water, clam juice, potatoes, and salt; bring to boil. Reduce heat; cover and simmer until potatoes are tender, about 10 minutes.

**2** Stir in cod and shrimp; cover and simmer until cod is just opaque throughout, about 3 minutes. Remove from heat and stir in cilantro. Serve with lime wedges.

**FYI** If you'd like, you can add 1 cup fresh or frozen corn kernels when you add the fish in step 2.

ASIAN SHRIMP
AND RICE BOWLS

# Asian Shrimp and Rice Bowls

SERVES 4

UNDER 20 MINUTES

▲ 1 cup quick-cooking brown rice

3 tablespoons rice vinegar

3 tablespoons ponzu sauce

2 teaspoons Asian (dark) sesame oil

1½ teaspoons grated peeled fresh ginger

1 teaspoon Sriracha (Asian hot chile sauce)

▲ 1 pound medium peeled and deveined cooked shrimp

▲ 1 cucumber, halved lengthwise, seeded, and cut into matchstick strips

▲ 2 medium carrots, cut into matchstick strips

▲ 4 large radishes, cut into matchstick strips

▲ 1 cup bean sprouts

⅓ cup fresh whole cilantro leaves

**PER SERVING (1 bowl):**
212 Cal, 4 g Total Fat, 1 g Sat Fat,
0 g Trans Fat, 168 mg Chol,
495 mg Sod, 23 g Carb, 3 g Sugar,
3 g Fib, 21 g Prot, 67 mg Calc.

**1** Cook rice according to package directions, omitting salt and butter. Transfer to a large bowl and let stand to cool 10 minutes.

**2** Meanwhile, to make dressing, whisk together vinegar, ponzu sauce, sesame oil, ginger, and Sriracha sauce in small bowl.

**3** Divide rice among 4 shallow serving bowls. Arrange shrimp, cucumber, carrots, radishes, and bean sprouts on rice. Drizzle evenly with dressing and sprinkle with cilantro.

**FYI** Ponzu sauce is a citrusy soy sauce and Sriracha is a fiery red chile sauce. Look for both of these in the Asian foods section of supermarkets.

# Vietnamese Rice Noodle Salad with Grilled Shrimp

SERVES 4

4 ounces thin rice noodles

▲ ¼ cup minced red onion

2 tablespoons rice vinegar

1 tablespoon Asian fish sauce

1 teaspoon sugar

¼ teaspoon red pepper flakes

▲ 1 pound large shrimp, peeled and deveined

¼ teaspoon salt

▲ 6 radishes, chopped

▲ 1 large carrot, coarsely shredded

▲ ½ small head Napa cabbage, thinly sliced (about 3 cups)

1 cup fresh basil leaves, torn

¾ cup fresh whole mint leaves

2 tablespoons unsalted dry-roasted peanuts, coarsely chopped

Lime wedges

**PER SERVING** (1½ cups salad with about 6 shrimp): 245 Cal, 3 g Total Fat, 1 g Sat Fat, 0 g Trans Fat, 168 mg Chol, 714 mg Sod, 32 g Carb, 3 g Sugar, 3 g Fib, 21 g Prot, 116 mg Calc.

**1** Cook rice noodles according to package directions. Drain, rinse with cold water, and drain again.

**2** Meanwhile, to make dressing, stir together onion, vinegar, fish sauce, sugar, and red pepper flakes in large bowl until sugar dissolves. Set aside.

**3** Sprinkle shrimp with salt. Spray ridged grill pan with nonstick spray and heat over medium heat. Place shrimp in grill pan and cook until just opaque in center, about 2 minutes on each side. Transfer to plate.

**4** Add noodles, radishes, carrot, cabbage, basil, and mint to dressing and toss to combine. Divide noodle mixture among 4 serving plates; top evenly with shrimp. Sprinkle with peanuts and serve with lime wedges.

**FYI** If you don't have rice noodles, you can make this salad with whole wheat angel hair pasta.

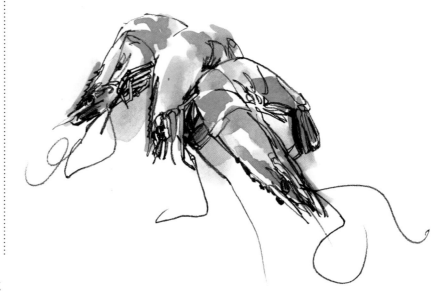

# Pan-Seared Scallops with Tomato-Orange Sauce

SERVES 4

4 teaspoons olive oil

▲ 4 leeks, halved lengthwise and thinly sliced (white and light green parts only)

▲ 1 (14 1/2-ounce) can diced tomatoes

▲ 1 yellow bell pepper, thinly sliced

2 garlic cloves, minced

1 teaspoon grated orange zest

1/2 cup fresh orange juice

1/4 teaspoon plus 1/8 teaspoon salt

3 tablespoons chopped fresh basil

▲ 1 pound sea scallops (about 16)

1/8 teaspoon black pepper

2 tablespoons black olive tapenade

PER SERVING (4 scallops with 3/4 cup sauce):
262 Cal, 7 g Total Fat, 1 g Sat Fat, 0 g Trans Fat, 37 mg Chol, 782 mg Sod, 27 g Carb, 8 g Sugar, 3 g Fib, 22 g Prot, 111 mg Calc.

**1** To make sauce, heat 2 teaspoons oil in large nonstick skillet over medium-low heat. Add leeks; cover and cook, stirring occasionally, until softened, about 10 minutes. Stir in tomatoes, bell pepper, garlic, orange zest and juice, and 1/4 teaspoon salt; bring to boil. Reduce heat; cover and simmer until vegetables are soft, about 10 minutes. Stir in basil.

**2** About 5 minutes before sauce is done, sprinkle scallops with pepper and remaining 1/8 teaspoon salt. Heat remaining 2 teaspoons oil in large heavy skillet over medium-high heat. Add scallops and cook until lightly browned and just opaque in center, 2–3 minutes on each side.

**3** Spoon sauce evenly onto 4 serving plates; top evenly with scallops. Spoon a small amount of tapenade onto each scallop and serve at once.

**FYI** Serve the scallops with a side of whole wheat linguine to soak up all the delicious juices from the sauce. A 1/2-cup serving of cooked whole wheat linguine will increase the *PointsPlus* value by *2*.

# Clams Steamed with Sausage, Potatoes, and Greens

SERVES 4

¾ pound hot Italian turkey sausage, casings removed

▲ 1 onion, chopped

3 garlic cloves, minced

▲ 2 cups reduced-sodium chicken broth

▲ 1 (10-ounce) box frozen chopped kale

▲ ¾ pound Yukon gold potatoes, cut into 1-inch chunks

▲ 24 littleneck clams, scrubbed

1 teaspoon butter

**PER SERVING (1¼ cups):**
346 Cal, 12 g Total Fat, 1 g Sat Fat,
0 g Trans Fat, 91 mg Chol,
666 mg Sod, 28 g Carb, 5 g Sugar,
4 g Fib, 36 g Prot, 179 mg Calc.

**1** Spray large heavy skillet with nonstick spray and set over medium-high heat. Add sausage and onion and cook, stirring frequently to break up sausage, until browned, about 8 minutes. Add garlic and cook, stirring constantly, until fragrant, 30 seconds.

**2** Add broth, kale, and potatoes and bring to boil. Reduce heat; cover and simmer, stirring occasionally to break up kale, until potatoes are tender, about 15 minutes.

**3** Increase heat to medium-high and add clams. Cover and cook until shells open, about 8 minutes. Discard any clams that do not open. Stir in butter.

# Crab and Quinoa Salad

SERVES 4

▲ ³/₄ cup quinoa, rinsed

1¹/₂ cups water

3 tablespoons sherry vinegar

2 teaspoons olive oil

2 teaspoons honey

¹/₂ teaspoon salt

▲ 2 (6-ounce) cans lump crabmeat, drained

▲ 3 scallions, thinly sliced

▲ 2 large ripe plums, pitted and diced

▲ 2 celery stalks, thinly sliced

▲ 1 carrot, grated

▲ 6 cups baby greens

2 tablespoons slivered almonds, toasted

**PER SERVING** (1¹/₂ cups greens with about 1¹/₂ cups crab mixture): 287 Cal, 7 g Total Fat, 1 g Sat Fat, 0 g Trans Fat, 60 mg Chol, 668 mg Sod, 34 g Carb, 9 g Sugar, 6 g Fib, 25 g Prot, 108 mg Calc.

**1** Combine quinoa and water in small saucepan; bring to boil. Reduce heat; cover and simmer until liquid is absorbed and quinoa is tender, about 12 minutes. Spoon quinoa onto large plate and let stand to cool.

**2** Whisk together vinegar, oil, honey, and salt in large bowl. Add crabmeat, scallions, plums, celery, carrot, and quinoa; toss to combine. Divide greens among 4 serving plates. Top evenly with crab mixture and sprinkle with almonds.

**FYI** When plums are not in season, you can substitute chopped fresh mango or orange segments in this recipe.

# Grilled Squid Salad with Creamy Chipotle Dressing

SERVES 4

UNDER 20 MINUTES

3 tablespoons reduced-fat chipotle mayonnaise

2 tablespoons lemon juice

1 teaspoon Asian (dark) sesame oil

1 teaspoon water

▲ 1 pound squid

1 teaspoon grated lemon zest

1/8 teaspoon salt

▲ 1  red onion, halved and cut into 1/2-inch wedges

▲ 1 (5-ounce) container baby arugula or spinach

▲ 1 mango, peeled and thinly sliced

PER SERVING (1 plate):
190 Cal, 5 g Total Fat, 1 g Sat Fat,
0 g Trans Fat, 264 mg Chol,
232 mg Sod, 18 g Carb, 11 g Sugar,
2 g Fib, 19 g Prot, 106 mg Calc.

5 PointsPlus® value

**1**  To make dressing, whisk together mayonnaise, 1 tablespoon lemon juice, sesame oil, and water in small bowl. Set aside.

**2**  Combine squid, lemon zest, salt, and remaining 1 tablespoon lemon juice in medium bowl and toss to coat.

**3**  Spray ridged grill pan with nonstick spray; set over medium heat until hot. Add onion and cook until tender, turning once, about 5 minutes. Remove onion to plate. Increase heat to high. Add squid to grill pan and cook in batches until just opaque, turning once, about 1 minute on each side. Transfer to cutting board. Thinly slice squid bodies and tentacles.

**4**  Toss together arugula, mango, and grilled onion in large bowl; divide evenly among 4 serving plates. Top evenly with squid and drizzle with dressing.

**FYI**  Squid cooks very quickly. Watch it carefully as it cooks and remove it from the grill pan as soon as it becomes opaque. If squid is not a favorite, you can make this salad with shrimp instead.

**GRILLED SQUID SALAD WITH
CREAMY CHIPOTLE DRESSING**

# Vegetarian

## Main Dishes

# Vegetarian

1 to 2 servings per day of lean protein; 1¹/₂ cups of cooked dried beans or 1¹/₂ cups of shelled edamame or 3 ounces of tofu counts as 1 serving.

## WHY THEY'RE ESSENTIAL

**Vegetarian meals are almost always healthier.** Even if you're not vegetarian, try eating at least a couple of vegetarian meals each week. You'll most likely consume more vegetables and whole grains and less cholesterol and saturated fat, not to mention meatless meals may be less expensive than those centered on meat.

**Soy is super.** Soy foods, such as tofu and edamame, may help prevent heart disease by lowering "bad" LDL cholesterol. Eating soy may help reduce some symptoms of menopause and may reduce the likelihood of developing prostate cancer.

**Beans are full of nutrients.** Beans, such as garbanzo, kidney, cannellini, black, and navy (cooked from dried or canned), are one of the best sources of plant protein, with about 6 grams in each ¹/₂ cup (about as much protein as in 1 egg). They're terrific for fiber too—about 6 grams of fiber in ¹/₂ cup. Dried beans are a good source of B vitamins, iron, calcium, and potassium and have virtually no fat.

**Vegetaian meals can help the environment.** By consuming more plants and less meat, you'll help reduce greenhouse gas emissions, minimize water use, and reduce fossil fuel used in livestock production.

## WHAT TO BUY

**Tofu:** Regular and low-fat tofu are both power foods.

*TIP: Choose extra-firm or firm tofu for stir-fries, grilling, baking, or sautéing. Soft tofu is good in smoothies and desserts. Silken tofu is good for making smoothies or creamy sauces or salad dressings.*

**Edamame:** Buy frozen in the pod or shelled edamame. Look for fresh soybeans at summer farmers' markets.

*TIP: A 10-ounce bag of shelled edamame is about 2 cups.*

**Dried Beans:** Buy dried beans and cook them yourself for an economical alternative or, for convenience, purchase canned beans.

*TIP: If you're watching your sodium, look for no-salt-added or reduced-sodium varieties of canned beans.*

## GOOD TO KNOW

**It's easy to get plenty of protein.** If you're eating a variety of healthful foods, even if you are a full-time vegetarian, you're almost certainly consuming enough protein.

**Nix the mix.** You don't have to eat certain foods together at a vegetarian meal to get complete proteins. If you're enjoying an assortment of plant foods throughout the day and meeting your energy needs, your body will have all the proteins and amino acids it needs.

## Regular or low-fat tofu

### POWER-UP IDEAS

- Add soft tofu to your favorite smoothie recipe to boost the protein and make you feel fuller longer.

- Substitute cubes of firm tofu for beef, pork, or chicken in stir-fry recipes.

- Tofu takes on the flavor of the seasonings you cook it with; no rules say it has to be Asian. Try seasoning it with chili powder, Italian herbs, or Cajun spices.

### TAKE NOTE

- Unlike animal protein, tofu contains no cholesterol and is low in saturated fat.

- Tofu is an excellent source of iron and a good source of omega-3 fatty acids.

- Many brands of tofu are enriched with calcium. If you don't eat much dairy, tofu is a great option for getting this essential mineral.

- A 3-ounce serving of low-fat tofu has just *1 PointsPlus* value.

## Edamame

### POWER-UP IDEAS

- Enjoy edamame in the pod for an afternoon snack.

- Add shelled edamame to soups and salads.

- Puree shelled edamame and season with garlic and lemon zest and juice for a tasty dip.

- Add shelled edamame to a vegetable stir-fry to make a protein-rich main dish.

### TAKE NOTE

- Edamame is an excellent source of fiber, with 4 grams in each ½ cup serving.

- Essential nutrients found in edamame include folic acid, manganese, and vitamin K.

- ½ cup of edamame has 8 grams of protein, as much as in an ounce of ground beef.

- ½ cup of shelled edamame has *2 PointsPlus* value.

## Dried beans

### POWER-UP IDEAS

- Make your own fat-free refried beans by mashing canned beans with a potato masher and heating in a nonstick skillet with a bit of vegetable broth.

- Add cooked dried beans to burritos, enchiladas, salsas, salads, and soups.

- Make low-fat hummus your go-to snack. It's high in fiber and protein and will keep you going through the afternoon.

### TAKE NOTE

- Because of the high fiber in beans, they take longer to digest, making you feel fuller longer.

- Dried beans, particularly black beans, contain antioxidants, which can help prevent heart disease and certain cancers.

- Varieties of white beans have almost twice the amount of iron as black beans.

## In this chapter

ORANGE TEMPEH AND
VEGETABLE STIR-FRY

2 tablespoons orange juice

1¹/₂ teaspoons cornstarch

1 tablespoon Asian (dark) sesame oil

▲ 3 scallions, minced

2 garlic cloves, minced

1 tablespoon minced peeled
fresh ginger

▲ 12 ounces snow peas, trimmed

▲ 1 yellow or red bell pepper,
thinly sliced

8 ounces tempeh, cut into
¹/₂-inch slices

▲ ¹/₂ cup reduced-sodium
vegetable broth

2 tablespoons reduced-sodium
soy sauce

1 tablespoon hoisin sauce

1 tablespoon grated orange zest

**PER SERVING (1¹/₄ cups):**
212 Cal, 10 g Total Fat, 2 g Sat Fat,
0 g Trans Fat, 0 mg Chol,
361 mg Sod, 20 g Carb, 6 g Sugar,
4 g Fib, 14 g Prot, 122 mg Calc.

# Orange Tempeh and Vegetable Stir-Fry

**1** Stir together orange juice and cornstarch in small bowl. Set aside.

**2** Heat large heavy skillet or wok over medium-high heat until drop of water sizzles in pan. Add oil and swirl to coat pan. Add scallions, garlic, and ginger; stir-fry until scallions begin to soften, 30 seconds. Add peas and bell pepper; stir-fry until peas turn bright green, 1 minute.

**3** Add tempeh; stir-fry until heated through, 2 minutes. Stir in broth, soy sauce, hoisin sauce, and orange zest and bring to boil. Add orange juice mixture and stir until mixture is thickened and bubbling, about 1 minute.

**FYI** Serve the stir-fry with brown rice (²/₃ cup cooked brown rice per serving will increase the **PointsPlus** value by **3**).

*Vegetarian*

▲ ²/₃ cup soft tofu

1 cup water

1 (5-ounce) package falafel mix

1 tablespoon olive oil

▲ 1 medium tomato, chopped

▲ ¹/₂ cup chopped cucumber

▲ ¹/₄ cup chopped celery

¹/₄ cup chopped fresh
flat-leaf parsley

2 tablespoons rice vinegar

1 small garlic clove, minced

▲ 1 (5-ounce) package mixed
salad greens

**PER SERVING (1³/₄ cups salad
with 3 falafel patties):**
185 Cal, 6 g Total Fat, 1 g Sat Fat,
0 g Trans Fat, 0 mg Chol,
606 mg Sod, 23 g Carb, 5 g Sugar,
7 g Fib, 15 g Prot, 112 mg Calc.

# Tofu-Falafel Salad

**1**  Combine tofu and water in food processor and process until smooth. Transfer to medium bowl and stir in falafel mix. Let stand just until mixture is moistened, 8–10 minutes. Shape falafel mixture into 12 (2 ¹/₂-inch) patties.

**2**  Heat oil in 12-inch nonstick skillet over medium heat. Add falafel patties and cook, until golden brown, 3–4 minutes on each side.

**3**  Meanwhile, stir together tomato, cucumber, celery, parsley, vinegar, and garlic in large bowl. Just before serving, add salad greens and toss to coat.

**4**  Divide salad evenly among 4 plates; top each salad with 3 falafel patties and serve at once.

**FYI**  **To add more color and flavor to the salad, you can add a chopped red or green bell pepper.**

# Black Bean and Tofu Enchiladas

SERVES 4

8 dried New Mexico red chile peppers, seeded and torn into pieces

▲ 1 onion, chopped

2 garlic cloves, minced

▲ 2 ⅓ cups reduced-sodium vegetable broth

1 tablespoon minced fresh oregano or 2 teaspoons dried

¼ teaspoon salt

¼ teaspoon black pepper

▲ 1 ½ (14-ounce) packages firm tofu, diced

▲ 1 (15 ½-ounce) can black beans, rinsed and drained

▲ 1 (10-ounce) can diced tomatoes with mild chiles, drained

1 teaspoon ground cumin

4 (8-inch) whole wheat tortillas

PER SERVING (1 enchilada plus 2 tablespoons sauce):
418 Cal, 14 g Total Fat, 1 g Sat Fat, 0 g Trans Fat, 0 mg Chol, 877 mg Sod, 57 g Carb, 5 g Sugar, 23 g Fib, 30 g Prot, 383 mg Calc.

**11** PointsPlus® value

1 Heat large skillet over medium-low heat. Add chile pieces; toast until fragrant, turning occasionally, about 4 minutes. Transfer to plate.

2 Spray same skillet with nonstick spray and set over medium heat. Add onion and garlic; cook, stirring constantly, until onion is softened, 5 minutes. Add reserved chiles, broth, oregano, salt, and pepper and bring to boil. Reduce heat, cover, and simmer 20 minutes. Remove from heat. Let cool slightly. Transfer chile mixture to food processor and process until smooth. Set aside ½ cup of sauce for serving. Spoon remaining sauce into large bowl.

3 Preheat oven to 400°F. Spray 9 x 13-inch baking dish with nonstick spray.

4 Stir together tofu, beans, tomatoes, and cumin in large bowl. Working with one tortilla at a time, dip each tortilla into sauce, and place on large plate. Spoon about ⅔ cup tofu mixture onto tortilla. Roll up and place seam side down in baking dish. Repeat with remaining tortillas and tofu mixture. Pour sauce remaining in large bowl over enchiladas.

5 Bake until sauce is bubbling, about 15 minutes. Let stand 5 minutes before serving. Serve enchiladas with reserved ½ cup sauce.

FYI You can add more vegetables to this meal by serving the enchiladas with a chopped salad made with chopped tomatoes, cucumber, red onion, and cilantro tossed with lime juice and salt and pepper to taste.

# Spicy Tofu Stir-Fry with Broccolini and Cashews

SERVES 4

4 teaspoons canola oil

▲ 1 (14-ounce) package firm tofu, drained, patted dry, and cut into 1-inch cubes

▲ 2 large bell peppers, thinly sliced

▲ ¼ cup chopped red onion

2 garlic cloves, minced

1 tablespoon minced peeled fresh ginger

▲ 1 bunch (8 ounces) broccolini, trimmed and left whole

⅓ cup water

1 tablespoon reduced-sodium soy sauce

2 teaspoons chili-garlic sauce

2 tablespoons unsalted cashews, coarsely chopped

**PER SERVING (1¼ cups):**
203 Cal, 12 g Total Fat, 1 g Sat Fat, 0 g Trans Fat, 0 mg Chol, 212 mg Sod, 14 g Carb, 4 g Sugar, 3 g Fib, 13 g Prot, 245 mg Calc.

1  Heat 12-inch large heavy skillet or wok over medium-high heat until drop of water sizzles in pan; add 2 teaspoons oil and swirl to coat pan. Add tofu and cook, turning often, until lightly browned on all sides, about 5 minutes. Transfer tofu to plate.

2  Heat remaining 2 teaspoons oil over medium-high heat in same skillet. Add bell peppers and stir-fry until crisp-tender, 3 minutes. Add onion, garlic and ginger; stir-fry until fragrant, 30 seconds. Add broccolini and stir-fry until bright green, 2 minutes. Add water; cover and cook until broccolini is crisp-tender, 5 minutes.

3  Add tofu, soy sauce, and chili-garlic sauce; stir-fry until tofu is heated through, about 2 minutes. Sprinkle with cashews.

**FYI**  Broccolini is a cross between regular broccoli and Chinese broccoli. It has long, thin stems and a slightly milder flavor than regular broccoli. You can substitute regular broccoli in this recipe, but reduce the cooking time by two to three minutes.

SPICY TOFU STIR-FRY WITH
BROCCOLINI AND CASHEWS

# Edamame and Chickpea Salad with Miso Dressing

SERVES 4

▲ 1 (10-ounce) package frozen edamame

1 ½ tablespoons white miso

½ teaspoon grated lemon zest

2 tablespoons lemon juice

2 tablespoons orange juice

1 tablespoon olive oil

½ teaspoon grated peeled fresh ginger

▲ 1 (15½-ounce) can chickpeas, rinsed and drained

▲ ½ English (seedless) cucumber, halved lengthwise and sliced

▲ 1 medium carrot, coarsely shredded

▲ 2 tablespoons chopped red onion

1　Bring medium saucepan of water to boil. Add edamame and cook 5 minutes; drain and rinse under cold water.

2　Whisk together miso, lemon zest and juice, orange juice, oil, and ginger in large bowl until smooth. Add edamame, chickpeas, cucumber, carrot, and onion and stir to combine. Let stand at room temperature 15 minutes before serving, or cover and refrigerate up to 2 hours and serve chilled.

FYI　To add even more color and flavor to this salad, you can add a chopped red bell pepper and 2 tablespoons chopped fresh cilantro.

PER SERVING (1 cup):
221 Cal, 8 g Total Fat, 1 g Sat Fat,
0 g Trans Fat, 0 mg Chol,
392 mg Sod, 26 g Carb, 6 g Sugar,
8 g Fib, 13 g Prot, 79 mg Calc

5 PointsPlus® value

# White Bean and Roasted Garlic Soufflé

SERVES 4

1 head garlic

▲ 1 (15½-ounce) can cannellini (white kidney) beans, rinsed and drained

6 fresh sage leaves

2 large egg yolks

2 ounces reduced-fat Swiss cheese, finely shredded

▲ 4 large egg whites, at room temperature

**PER SERVING (1¼ cups):**
176 Cal, 3 g Total Fat, 1 g Sat Fat, 0 g Trans Fat, 110 mg Chol, 385 mg Sod, 21 g Carb, 2 g Sugar, 5 g Fib, 16 g Prot, 217 mg Calc.

4
PointsPlus
value

1 Preheat oven to 375°F. Wrap garlic in foil and bake until soft and fragrant, about 1 hour. Unwrap garlic and let stand until cool enough to handle. Maintain oven temperature.

2 Spray 1-quart soufflé dish with nonstick spray.

3 Squeeze out garlic pulp. Combine garlic pulp, beans, and sage in food processor and puree. Add egg yolks and pulse until combined. Transfer mixture to large bowl. Stir in cheese.

4 With electric mixer on high speed, beat egg whites in large bowl until soft peaks form, 1–2 minutes. Stir ¼ of egg whites into bean mixture to lighten. Gently fold in remaining whites in 2 additions until just mixed.

5 Spoon mixture into dish and bake until soufflé is puffed and lightly browned, 30 minutes. Serve at once.

**FYI** To make a colorful green salad to serve with the soufflé, toss together 1 cup each of torn romaine, radicchio, Belgian endive, and arugula with white-wine vinegar and salt and pepper to taste.

# Chinese Red-Cooked Tofu

SERVES 4

▲ 1 cup reduced-sodium vegetable broth

▲ 2 celery stalks, diced

▲ 2 scallions, chopped

▲ 1 carrot, diced

¼ cup reduced-sodium soy sauce

2 tablespoons rice vinegar

2 tablespoons Shaoxing (Chinese cooking wine) or dry sherry

2 teaspoons honey

½ teaspoon five-spice powder

▲ 1 (14-ounce) package firm tofu, drained and cubed

2 teaspoons cornstarch

2 teaspoons water

**PER SERVING (1¼ cups):**
144 Cal, 5 g Total Fat, 1 g Sat Fat, 0 g Trans Fat, 0 mg Chol, 609 mg Sod, 13 g Carb, 5 g Sugar, 2 g Fib, 10 g Prot, 220 mg Calc.

**1** Combine broth, celery, scallions, carrot, soy sauce, vinegar, wine, honey, and five-spice powder in large saucepan; bring to simmer over medium heat. Cover, reduce heat, and simmer until vegetables are tender, 10 minutes.

**2** Add tofu and simmer just until heated through, 2 minutes.

**3** Whisk together cornstarch and water in small bowl. Stir into tofu mixture and simmer until sauce is slightly thickened, about 1 minute longer.

**FYI** Red cooking is a Chinese method of braising using soy sauce, wine, and sugar. It produces dishes that are coated in a rich and flavorful burgundy-colored sauce. To make this a more filling meal, add 1 large thinly sliced red bell pepper with the celery in step 1. Serve the tofu and vegetables with brown rice (⅔ cup cooked brown rice per serving will increase the **PointsPlus** value by **3**).

# Tofu-Corn Soup with Roasted Pepper Puree

SERVES 4

2 teaspoons olive oil

▲ 2 celery stalks, chopped

▲ 1 onion, chopped

▲ 4 cups fresh corn kernels or frozen corn

▲ 3 cups reduced-sodium vegetable broth

1 tablespoon minced fresh tarragon

2 teaspoons Worcestershire sauce

½ teaspoon salt

½ teaspoon black pepper

▲ 1 roasted red pepper, drained and chopped (not oil packed)

1 tablespoon balsamic vinegar

▲ ½ (14-ounce) package silken tofu, drained and cubed

**PER SERVING** (1½ cups soup and 2 tablespoons puree): 213 Cal, 5 g Total Fat, 1 g Sat Fat, 0 g Trans Fat, 0 mg Chol, 532 mg Sod, 38 g Carb, 10 g Sugar, 6 g Fib, 8 g Prot, 77 mg Calc.

**6 PointsPlus value**

1   Heat oil in large saucepan over medium heat. Add celery and onion; cook, stirring occasionally, until softened, 5 minutes. Add corn, broth, tarragon, Worcestershire sauce, salt, and pepper; bring to boil. Reduce heat and simmer, covered, until vegetables are very tender, 10 minutes. Let cool slightly.

2   Meanwhile, combine roasted bell pepper and vinegar in food processor and process until smooth. Set aside.

3   Pour soup, in batches, into blender and puree, adding tofu to one of the batches. Return soup to saucepan and cook over low heat, stirring often, until hot, about 2 minutes. Ladle soup evenly into 4 bowls and top evenly with red pepper puree.

# French Lentil and Goat Cheese Salad with Dill

SERVES 4

6 cups water

▲ 1 cup green (French) lentils, picked over, rinsed, and drained

3/4 teaspoon salt

▲ 2 celery stalks including green leaves, diced

▲ 2 carrots, cut into matchstick-thin strips

1 shallot, minced

3 tablespoons white-wine vinegar

2 tablespoons minced fresh dill

1 tablespoon olive oil

1 tablespoon Dijon mustard

1/2 teaspoon black pepper

3 ounces goat cheese, crumbled

**1** Bring water, lentils, and 1/2 teaspoon salt to boil in large saucepan. Reduce heat and simmer, uncovered, until lentils are tender but hold their shape, 15–20 minutes. Drain; transfer to large bowl to cool.

**2** Add celery, carrots, shallot, vinegar, dill, oil, mustard, pepper, and remaining 1/4 teaspoon salt to lentils and stir to combine. Stir in goat cheese just before serving. Serve chilled or at room temperature.

**FYI** You can make this salad even more filling by serving it on a bed of mixed greens.

PER SERVING (1 1/2 cups):
263 Cal, 9 g Total Fat, 4 g Sat Fat,
0 g Trans Fat, 10 mg Chol,
676 mg Sod, 33 g Carb, 3 g Sugar,
8 g Fib, 14 g Prot, 86 mg Calc.

**7** PointsPlus value

FRENCH LENTIL AND GOAT CHEESE
SALAD WITH DILL

# Black-Eyed Peas and Collard Greens

SERVES 4

2 teaspoons olive oil

2 garlic cloves, thinly sliced

¼ teaspoon red pepper flakes

▲ 8 cups chopped fresh collard greens

¼ cup dry white wine or dry vermouth

▲ 1 cup reduced-sodium vegetable broth

▲ 2 (15½-ounce) cans black-eyed peas, rinsed and drained

¼ teaspoon black pepper

⅛ teaspoon salt

1 tablespoon apple-cider vinegar

PER SERVING (2 cups): 236 Cal, 3 g Total Fat, 0 g Sat Fat, 0 g Trans Fat, 0 mg Chol, 865 mg Sod, 38 g Carb, 0 g Sugar, 10 g Fib, 11 g Prot, 143 mg Calc.

1  Heat oil in large skillet over medium heat. Add garlic and red pepper flakes and cook, stirring constantly, until fragrant, 30 seconds. Add collards in batches and cook, stirring often, until wilted, 2 minutes.

2  Add wine and bring to boil. Reduce heat and simmer until almost all liquid is evaporated, about 3 minutes. Add broth, cover, and simmer 10 minutes.

3  Add peas, pepper, and salt; cover and simmer until almost all liquid is absorbed and collards are tender, 30 minutes. Remove from heat and stir in vinegar.

FYI  You can add 1½ cups diced celery, fennel, carrots, or parsnips (or a combination) when you add the peas.

2 teaspoons olive oil

1 shallot, minced

1 garlic clove, minced

▲ 1 (15½-ounce) can pinto beans,
rinsed and drained

½ cup old-fashioned oats

▲ 1 large egg white

2 tablespoons slivered almonds

2 tablespoons chopped fresh cilantro

1 teaspoon ground cumin

½ teaspoon salt

½ teaspoon black pepper

**PER SERVING** (1 patty):
182 Cal, 5 g Total Fat, 1 g Sat Fat,
0 g Trans Fat, 0 mg Chol,
636 mg Sod, 25 g Carb, 1 g Sugar,
7 g Fib, 8 g Prot, 52 mg Calc.

# Southwest Bean Burgers

1   Heat oil in small skillet over medium heat. Add shallot and garlic and cook, stirring often, until softened, 2 minutes. Transfer mixture to food processor.

2   Add beans, oats, egg white, almonds, cilantro, cumin, salt, and pepper to food processor. Pulse until combined. Shape mixture into 4 (4-inch) patties.

3   Spray a large nonstick skillet with nonstick spray and set over medium heat. Add patties and cook until well browned, about 3 minutes on each side.

**FYI**   You can serve these vegetarian burgers on a bed of flavorful cucumbers to add color and crunch. To make them, toss thinly sliced cucumbers and red onion with whole cilantro leaves, lime juice, and salt and cayenne pepper to taste.

# Spanish Chickpea, Tomato, and Kale Stew

SERVES 4

1 tablespoon water

¼ teaspoon saffron threads

2 teaspoons olive oil

▲ 1 onion, chopped

▲ 1 green bell pepper, chopped

2 garlic cloves, minced

2 tablespoons minced fresh oregano

1 tablespoon smoked or regular paprika

▲ 4 cups chopped fresh kale

¼ cup dry sherry

▲ 1 (15½-ounce) can chickpeas, rinsed and drained

▲ 1 (14½-ounce) can diced tomatoes

▲ 1 cup reduced-sodium vegetable broth

½ teaspoon black pepper

¼ teaspoon salt

**PER SERVING (1½ cups):**
214 Cal, 4 g Total Fat, 0 g Sat Fat, 0 g Trans Fat, 0 mg Chol, 722 mg Sod, 36 g Carb, 9 g Sugar, 8 g Fib, 8 g Prot, 159 mg Calc.

**1** Combine water and saffron in small bowl; set aside.

**2** Meanwhile, heat oil in large saucepan over medium heat. Add onion and bell pepper and cook, stirring often, until vegetables are softened, 5 minutes. Stir in garlic, oregano, paprika, and saffron with soaking water.

**3** Add kale and cook, stirring constantly, until wilted, 1 minute. Add sherry and cook until almost all liquid evaporates, 3 minutes.

**4** Add chickpeas, tomatoes, broth, pepper, and salt and bring to boil. Cover, reduce heat, and simmer, stirring occasionally, until kale is tender, 30 minutes.

**FYI** To add even more vegetables to this stew, add chopped zucchini or yellow squash during the last 5 minutes of cooking.

SPANISH CHICKPEA,
TOMATO, AND KALE STEW

# Black Bean and Quinoa-Stuffed Peppers

SERVES 4

▲ ½ cup quinoa, rinsed

2 teaspoons olive oil

▲ ½ cup chopped sweet onion

▲ 1 medium tomato, chopped

▲ 1 cup fresh or frozen corn
kernels, thawed

1 tablespoon plus 1 teaspoon
chili powder

½ teaspoon ground cumin

¼ teaspoon salt

▲ 1 cup canned black beans,
rinsed and drained

▲ 4 large poblano peppers, halved
lengthwise and seeded

¼ cup water

½ cup shredded low-fat
Mexican cheese blend

**PER SERVING (2 stuffed pepper halves):**
256 Cal, 8 g Total Fat, 2 g Sat Fat,
0 g Trans Fat, 8 mg Chol,
504 mg Sod, 37 g Carb, 3 g Sugar,
8 g Fib, 12 g Prot, 251 mg Calc.

1  Preheat oven to 400°F. Spray 9 x 13-inch baking dish with nonstick spray.

2  Cook quinoa according to package directions. Fluff with a fork.

3  Meanwhile, to make filling, heat oil in large nonstick skillet over medium heat. Add onion and cook, stirring often, until softened, 5 minutes. Add tomato, corn, chili powder, cumin, and salt. Cook, stirring often, until corn is crisp-tender, 2 minutes. Remove from heat and stir in quinoa and beans.

4  Spoon about ⅓ cup of filling into each pepper. Arrange peppers in single layer in baking dish. Add water to baking dish; cover and bake 40 minutes. Uncover, sprinkle peppers with cheese and bake until cheese melts, about 5 minutes.

# Polenta and Bean Casserole

SERVES 6

▲ 1 (15½-ounce) can black beans, rinsed and drained

▲ 1 (14½-ounce) can diced tomatoes with green chiles

▲ 1 (10-ounce) box frozen corn kernels

▲ 1 yellow squash, chopped

▲ 1 cup frozen baby lima beans

▲ 1 cup fat-free salsa

1 tablespoon chili powder

2 teaspoons ground cumin

▲ 1 (16-ounce) tube prepared fat-free polenta, cut into 12 (½-inch) slices

1 cup shredded reduced-fat Monterey Jack cheese

**PER SERVING** (⅙ of casserole):
310 Cal, 5 g Total Fat, 2 g Sat Fat,
0 g Trans Fat, 10 mg Chol,
969 mg Sod, 51 g Carb, 5 g Sugar,
8 g Fib, 15 g Prot, 448 mg Calc.

**8** PointsPlus® value

1   Preheat oven to 400°F. Spray shallow 2 ½-quart baking dish with nonstick spray.

2   Combine beans, tomatoes, corn, squash, lima beans, salsa, chili powder, and cumin in large saucepan. Set over high heat and bring to boil. Reduce heat and simmer, covered, about 10 minutes. Transfer mixture to baking dish. Arrange polenta slices on top, overlapping slices if needed.

3   Bake until bubbly at edges, about 25 minutes. Sprinkle polenta with cheese and bake until cheese melts, about 3 minutes longer. Let stand 10 minutes before serving.

Vegetarian

**FARRO AND CHESTNUT-STUFFED PEPPERS WITH APPLE CIDER SAUCE**

# Farro and Chestnut–Stuffed Peppers with Apple Cider Sauce

SERVES 4

3 cups water

▲ ¾ cup farro

▲ 4 green bell peppers

1 (5-ounce) jar whole peeled and cooked chestnuts, chopped

▲ ½ cup minced celery

¼ cup dried cranberries, minced

2 teaspoons Worcestershire sauce

1 teaspoon dried thyme

1 teaspoon dried sage

½ teaspoon salt

½ teaspoon black pepper

1 cup apple cider

PER SERVING (1 stuffed pepper):
255 Cal, 1 g Total Fat, 0 g Sat Fat,
0 g Trans Fat, 0 mg Chol,
365 mg Sod, 58 g Carb, 8 g Sugar,
5 g Fib, 8 g Prot, 75 mg Calc.

7
PointsPlus
value

1   Bring water to boil in medium saucepan. Add farro. Reduce heat and simmer, covered, until farro is tender, about 25 minutes; drain.

2   Preheat oven to 350°F. Spray medium deep casserole or 2-quart soufflé dish with nonstick spray.

3   Cut a thin slice from tops of bell peppers; remove ribs and seeds. Stir together farro, chestnuts, celery, cranberries, Worcestershire sauce, thyme, sage, salt, and pepper in large bowl. Spoon farro mixture evenly into each bell pepper. Place peppers in casserole. Pour cider into casserole. Cover and bake until peppers are tender, 1 hour. Transfer peppers to large plate and cover to keep warm.

4   To make sauce, pour cooking liquid into medium saucepan and bring to boil over high heat. Boil, stirring occasionally, until sauce is reduced and thickened slightly, about 5 minutes. Spoon sauce over stuffed peppers.

FYI   You can bake the peppers in a large loaf pan instead of a baking dish. The peppers will easily stand upright in a row without tipping over.

# Kasha and Mushroom– Stuffed Cabbage

SERVES 4

1½ cups water

▲ ¾ cup kasha

▲ 8 ounces cremini mushrooms, finely chopped

½ teaspoon dried dill

½ teaspoon dried thyme

½ teaspoon salt

½ teaspoon black pepper

▲ 1 large egg white

▲ 8 large Savoy cabbage leaves

▲ 1⅓ cups canned tomato puree

▲ ½ cup reduced-sodium vegetable broth

1 tablespoon honey

1 tablespoon apple-cider vinegar

PER SERVING (2 rolls with 3 tablespoons sauce):
191 Cal, 1 g Total Fat, 0 g Sat Fat, 0 g Trans Fat, 0 mg Chol, 364 mg Sod, 40 g Carb, 9 g Sugar, 6 g Fib, 8 g Prot, 52 mg Calc.

**5** PointsPlus value

**1** Combine water and kasha in large saucepan; bring to boil. Reduce heat; cover and simmer until liquid is absorbed and kasha is tender, 8–10 minutes.

**2** Meanwhile, spray large skillet with nonstick spray; set over medium heat. Add mushrooms and cook, stirring occasionally, until tender, 5 minutes. Remove from heat and stir in kasha, dill, thyme, salt, and pepper. Set aside to cool. Stir in egg white.

**3** Bring large pot of water to boil over high heat. Add cabbage leaves and cook until wilted, about 2 minutes. Using tongs, remove leaves to colander. Rinse under cold running water; drain again and set aside.

**4** Trim center vein from each cabbage leaf and spoon about ¼ cup kasha mixture in center of each leaf. Fold in sides over filling and roll up.

**5** Whisk together tomato puree, broth, honey, and vinegar in large deep skillet. Arrange cabbage rolls in skillet in single layer, seam side down. Cover and simmer over low heat until cabbage is very tender, 20 minutes. Uncover and simmer until sauce thickens, about 5 minutes longer.

# Basil-Lime Bulgur and Bean Salad

1½ cups water

▲ ½ cup bulgur

▲ 4 cups small broccoli florets

2 teaspoons grated lime zest

¼ cup lime juice

1 tablespoon olive oil

1 teaspoon ground cumin

¼ teaspoon salt

▲ 1 (15-ounce) can navy beans or cannellini (white kidney) beans, rinsed and drained

▲ ¼ cup diced red onion

½ cup chopped fresh basil

½ cup crumbled reduced-fat feta cheese

**PER SERVING** (about 1 cup): 288 Cal, 7 g Total Fat, 2 g Sat Fat, 0 g Trans Fat, 5 mg Chol, 707 mg Sod, 44 g Carb, 1 g Sugar, 12 g Fib, 17 g Prot, 164 mg Calc.

**1** Bring 1 cup of water to boil in medium saucepan. Stir in bulgur. Remove saucepan from heat. Cover and let stand 30 minutes. Drain.

**2** Meanwhile, place broccoli and remaining ½ cup water in microwavable bowl; cover with wax paper. Microwave on High until broccoli is just tender, 2–3 minutes. Drain and let cool.

**3** Whisk together lime zest and juice, oil, cumin, and salt in large bowl. Add bulgur, broccoli, beans, onion, and basil; toss to combine. Sprinkle with feta cheese just before serving.

Vegetarian

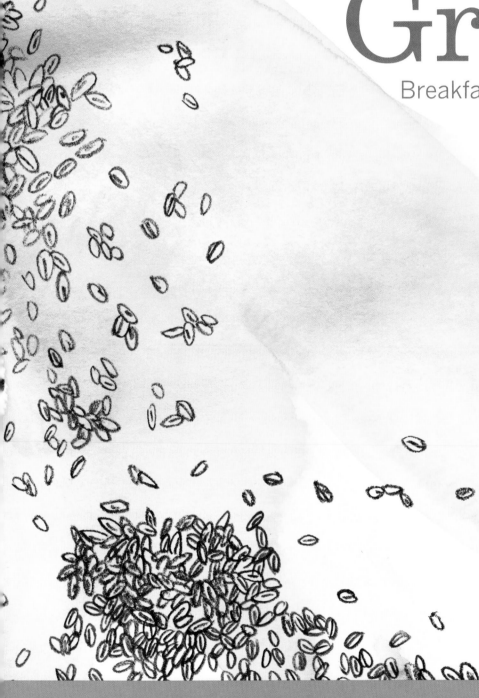

# Whole Grains

Breakfasts, Lunches, Sides,
and Desserts

# Whole Grains

## YOU NEED

Make whole grains your choice instead of refined white grains whenever possible.

## WHY THEY'RE ESSENTIAL

**Feast on fiber.** Whole grains are one of the best sources of fiber in the diet. Fiber is not only necessary for digestive health but it also lowers cholesterol.

**Grains really are great.** Whole grains contain many of the same antioxidants that are widely touted in fruits and vegetables. These antioxidants can reduce your risk of heart disease, stroke, diabetes, and certain kinds of cancer.

**Whole food is better for you.** You may be able to take dietary supplements to add some of the fiber and nutrients from whole grains to your diet, but consuming whole grains in their natural state allows the nutrients to work together in ways to protect your health that pills do not.

## WHAT TO BUY

**Whole grain wheat:** Look for bulgur, whole wheat couscous, farro, wheat berries, and fresh or dried whole wheat pasta.

*TIP: Cook grains in water or, to add more flavor, cook them in vegetable or chicken broth.*

**Whole grain rice:** Buy any variety of brown rice or wild rice, Bhutanese rice, or Wehani rice.

*TIP: Always rinse brown rice and other grains before cooking to remove any dirt or debris.*

**Corn products:** Cooked cornmeal (polenta); fat-free plain refrigerated polenta; grits; hominy; plain air-popped or light butter-flavored, reduced-fat microwave popcorn.

*TIP: Buy cornmeal, polenta, and grits that are labeled "whole corn" or "whole grain corn." If the label says "degermed" the germ has been removed and the product is not whole grain.*

**Other whole grains:** Amaranth, barley, millet, kasha (buckwheat), quinoa, whole grain pasta and noodles, brown rice udon noodles, soba noodles, and kamut, rye, or spelt pasta.

*TIP: Try pasta and noodles that are made with part whole grain and part refined grain until your taste buds adjust to the more robust flavors of whole grain versions.*

## GOOD TO KNOW

**Look for the stamp of approval.** An easy way to make sure you're getting 100% whole grains is to look for the rectangular yellow 100% Whole Grains stamp on packaged foods from the Whole Grains Council. It ensures that food is made from all whole grains. There is also a Basic Stamp that marks foods that are a good source of whole grains but also contain refined grains.

**Ease into whole grains.** Each type of whole grain has its own unique flavor and texture. When you begin to incorporate more whole grains in your diet, start with mild-flavored whole wheat couscous, bulgur, and quinoa and work your way up to bolder flavored grains such as wheat berries, farro, and wild rice.

# Whole grain wheat

## POWER-UP IDEAS

- Fine-grind bulgur, whole wheat couscous, and whole wheat pasta cook quickly enough to enjoy for a weeknight dinner.

- Use any cooked whole grain wheat product to serve as a side dish, to make a salad, or to add to soups or casseroles.

- Look for fresh whole wheat pasta, which cooks quicker than dried pasta.

## TAKE NOTE

- Bulgur is one of the most fiber-rich grains with 4 grams of fiber in ½ cup.

- Whole grains are better sources of minerals such as selenium and magnesium than refined grains.

- Because of its high-fiber and protein content, whole grain wheat is digested slowly and keeps you feeling fuller longer after you eat.

# Brown rice, wild rice

## POWER-UP IDEAS

- Cook a batch of brown rice on the weekend to serve with meals throughout the week.

- For convenience, try precooked or boil-in-bag brown rice or buy it from a local Chinese restaurant.

- Wild rice is expensive, but its unique nutty flavor and chewy texture make it worth the price.

## TAKE NOTE

- Whole grains, including brown rice, contain fiber which may help to lower the risk of heart disease.

- Phenols, abundant in brown rice, may be supportive in preventing cancer.

- Brown rice has less fiber than most other whole grains, but is an excellent source of vitamins and minerals.

# Corn products

## POWER-UP IDEAS

- Munch on air-popped popcorn for an after-noon or evening snack.

- Serve plain grits as a breakfast porridge or add a sprinkle of shredded cheese and serve them as a side dish.

- Add canned hominy to soups, salads, or chilis.

## TAKE NOTE

- Corn has 10 times the vitamin A of other grains.

- Popcorn is a Power Food and 3 cups of air-popped popcorn has only *2 PointsPlus* value.

- For those who have celiac disease, corn is an excellent gluten-free option.

# Other whole grains

## POWER-UP IDEAS

- Enjoy barley as a hot breakfast cereal, in soups or salads, or as a side dish.

- If you don't care for whole wheat pasta, try whole grain kamut, rye, or spelt pasta.

- To make muesli, stir together old-fashioned oats, fat-free plain yogurt, and chopped fruit. Let stand about 5 minutes to soften the oats and enjoy.

## TAKE NOTE

- Quinoa, a relative of Swiss chard and beets, contains complete protein with all the essential amino acids that our bodies need.

- Kasha (buckwheat) is high in protein, and minerals including zinc, manganese, and copper.

- Oats have more than 20 compounds that have antioxidant and anti-inflammatory properties.

# Dried Cherry-Almond Muesli

SERVES 6

▲ 2 ½ cups old-fashioned oats

▲ 1 cup fat-free milk

½ cup dried cherries

¼ cup unsweetened apple juice

▲ 1 cup plain fat-free yogurt

2 teaspoons packed light brown sugar

¼ cup slivered almonds, toasted

**PER SERVING** (½ cup):
238 Cal, 5 g Total Fat, 1 g Sat Fat,
0 g Trans Fat, 2 mg Chol,
51 mg Sod, 40 g Carb, 14 g Sugar,
5 g Fib, 10 g Prot, 153 mg Calc.

**1** Stir together oats, milk, cherries, and apple juice in medium bowl; let stand 30 minutes, stirring occasionally.

**2** Meanwhile, stir together yogurt and sugar in small bowl.

**3** Divide oat mixture evenly among 6 serving bowls. Top evenly with yogurt mixture and almonds.

**FYI** Fresh fruit makes a delicious addition to muesli. Add blueberries, sliced banana, or chopped apple, depending on what's in season.

# Orange-Pecan Couscous Breakfast Pudding

SERVES 6

1½ cups water

▲ 1 cup whole wheat couscous

Pinch salt

▲ 3 cups fat-free milk

2 tablespoons honey

½ teaspoon grated orange zest

▲ 1 large egg white

¼ cup toasted wheat germ

¾ teaspoon vanilla extract

3 tablespoons chopped pecans, toasted

PER SERVING (generous ¾ cup pudding and ½ tablespoon pecans):
178 Cal, 3 g Total Fat, 0 g Sat Fat, 0 g Trans Fat, 2 mg Chol, 81 mg Sod, 30 g Carb, 13 g Sugar, 4 g Fib, 9 g Prot, 165 mg Calc.

1  Bring water to boil in a large saucepan over high heat. Stir in couscous and salt. Reduce heat and simmer until water is absorbed, about 2 minutes. Remove saucepan from heat and fluff couscous with fork. Cover and let stand 5 minutes.

2  Whisk milk, honey, and orange zest into couscous. Bring to boil over medium-high heat, whisking frequently to break up any lumps. Reduce heat to medium-low and cook, stirring frequently, until mixture is slightly thickened, about 5 minutes. Remove saucepan from heat.

3  Whisk together ½ cup couscous mixture and egg white in small bowl. Add egg mixture to saucepan and cook over low heat, stirring, until pudding is thick and creamy, about 5 minutes longer.

4  Stir in wheat germ and vanilla. Spoon evenly into 6 serving bowls and sprinkle evenly with pecans.

FYI  You can top each serving of the pudding with a handful of fresh blueberries, raspberries, or strawberries.

▲ **3 cups fat-free milk**

1/8 **teaspoon ground cinnamon**

**Pinch salt**

▲ 1/2 **cup old-fashioned oats**

▲ 1/2 **cup quick-cooking barley**

▲ 1/2 **cup bulgur**

**2 teaspoons honey**

▲ **1 small apple, cored and chopped**

**2 tablespoons chopped walnuts**

**PER SERVING (1 bowl):**
302 Cal, 4 g Total Fat, 1 g Sat Fat,
0 g Trans Fat, 4 mg Chol,
119 mg Sod, 57 g Carb, 16 g Sugar,
9 g Fib, 13 g Prot, 250 mg Calc.

# Apple-Walnut Breakfast Porridge

1 Combine milk, cinnamon, and salt in medium saucepan and bring just to boil. Stir in oats, barley, and bulgur. Reduce heat and simmer, stirring often, until milk is absorbed and grains are tender, about 10 minutes.

2 Remove from heat and stir in honey. Spoon evenly into 4 serving bowls; sprinkle evenly with apple and walnuts.

**FYI** Porridge is any dish made with grains (usually oats) that are simmered in milk or water. It's usually served as a comforting and filling breakfast meal.

# Fruit and Nut Granola

**SERVES 10**

1½ cups old-fashioned oats

½ cup unprocessed wheat bran

¾ cup slivered almonds

⅓ cup honey

¼ teaspoon ground cinnamon

1 cup golden raisins

¼ cup toasted wheat germ

▲ 2½ cups fresh raspberries or blueberries

**PER SERVING** (½ cup granola and ¼ cup berries):
211 Cal, 6 g Total Fat, 1 g Sat Fat, 0 g Trans Fat, 0 mg Chol, 5 mg Sod, 38 g Carb, 23 g Sugar, 7 g Fib, 5 g Prot, 42 mg Calc.

1  Preheat oven to 350°F.

2  Spread oats and bran in large rimmed baking pan and bake, stirring often, until lightly browned, about 10 minutes.

3  Meanwhile, stir together almonds, honey, and cinnamon in large bowl. Add oat mixture and stir to combine. Spread mixture in same baking pan and bake, stirring often, until mixture is dark golden brown, about 10 minutes.

4  Transfer to bowl to cool. Stir in raisins and wheat germ. Just before serving, top each portion of granola with ¼ cup berries. The granola can be stored in an airtight container up to 2 weeks.

**FYI**  For an additional **2 PointsPlus** value, you can serve the granola with 1 cup fat-free milk, or for an additional **3 PointsPlus** value, enjoy it with 1 cup plain fat-free yogurt.

# Multigrain Blueberry Scones

1 cup all-purpose flour

3/4 cup whole wheat pastry flour

1/4 cup old-fashioned oats

▲ 1 tablespoon cornmeal

2 teaspoons baking powder

1/4 teaspoon baking soda

1/4 teaspoon salt

1/4 cup plus 2 tablespoons sugar

2 tablespoons unsalted butter, melted

▲ 1 large egg

1/2 cup low-fat buttermilk

1 teaspoon grated lemon zest

▲ 3/4 cup fresh or frozen blueberries

**PER SERVING (1 scone):**
256 Cal, 13 g Total Fat, 3 g Sat Fat,
0 g Trans Fat, 35 mg Chol,
275 mg Sod, 31 g Carb, 9 g Sugar,
2 g Fib, 5 g Prot, 55 mg Calc.

7 PointsPlus value

1 Preheat oven to 400°F. Line large baking sheet with parchment paper; spray paper with nonstick spray.

2 Whisk together flours, oats, cornmeal, baking powder, baking soda, and salt in medium bowl. Stir together 1/4 cup sugar and butter in another medium bowl until well mixed. Add egg, buttermilk, and lemon zest to sugar mixture and whisk until smooth.

3 Add half of flour mixture to sugar mixture and stir just until combined. Add remaining flour mixture and blueberries and stir just until moistened.

4 Spoon dough into center of pan. With well-floured hands, pat dough into 7-inch round. Spray a long, thin knife with nonstick spray; cut dough into 8 wedges, cutting into but not through the dough. Sprinkle scones with remaining 2 tablespoons sugar.

5 Bake until a toothpick inserted into center comes out clean, 20–22 minutes. Let cool on baking sheet on wire rack 5 minutes. Cut into wedges to serve. Serve warm or at room temperature.

**FYI** You can enjoy a scone along with yogurt for a satisfying breakfast (1 cup of plain fat-free yogurt will increase the *PointsPlus* value by *3*).

MAPLE-ALMOND QUINOA MUFFINS
PAGE 206, AND MULTIGRAIN
BLUEBERRY SCONES

# Maple-Almond Quinoa Muffins

SERVES 12

1 cup water

▲ ½ cup quinoa, rinsed

¾ cup low-fat (1%) milk

▲ 1 large egg

½ cup maple syrup

¼ cup almond oil or canola oil

1 teaspoon vanilla extract

1 cup whole wheat flour

1 cup quinoa flour

2 teaspoons baking powder

½ teaspoon salt

**PER SERVING (1 muffin):**
190 Cal, 6 g Total Fat, 1 g Sat Fat,
0 g Trans Fat, 19 mg Chol,
206 mg Sod, 29 g Carb, 9 g Sugar,
3 g Fib, 5 g Prot, 56 mg Calc.

**5 PointsPlus® value**

**1** Combine water and quinoa in small saucepan; bring to boil. Reduce heat; cover and simmer until liquid is absorbed and quinoa is tender, about 12 minutes. Spoon quinoa onto large plate and let stand to cool slightly.

**2** Meanwhile, preheat oven to 375°F. Spray 12-cup muffin pan with nonstick spray.

**3** Whisk together milk, egg, maple syrup, oil, vanilla, and quinoa in medium bowl. Whisk together flours, baking powder, and salt in large bowl. Add milk mixture to flour mixture and stir just until flour is moistened.

**4** Fill muffin cups evenly with batter. Bake until toothpick inserted into centers comes out clean, 18–20 minutes. Let cool in pan on wire rack 5 minutes. Remove muffins from pan and let cool completely on rack.

**FYI** Almond oil gives these muffins a delicate almond flavor. If you use canola oil instead, add ¼ teaspoon almond extract along with the vanilla extract. Look for quinoa flour in large supermarkets or in a health food store.

▲ 3 assorted color bell peppers

▲ 1 (15 ¹/₂-ounce) can black beans, rinsed and drained

▲ 1 cup fresh corn kernels or frozen corn, thawed

▲ ¹/₂ small red onion, minced

2 tablespoons lime juice

1 tablespoon olive oil

¹/₂ teaspoon ground chipotle chile powder

¹/₂ teaspoon ground cumin

¹/₂ teaspoon salt

PER SERVING (1 cup):
174 Cal, 5 g Total Fat, 1 g Sat Fat,
0 g Trans Fat, 0 mg Chol,
641 mg Sod, 28 g Carb, 4 g Sugar,
7 g Fib, 7 g Prot, 50 mg Calc.

# Bean and Corn Salad with Roasted Peppers

1  Preheat broiler. Spray baking sheet with nonstick spray. Place bell peppers on baking sheet and broil 5 inches from heat, turning occasionally, until lightly charred on all sides, about 5 minutes. Place peppers in paper bag and fold closed. Let steam 5 minutes. When cool enough to handle, peel peppers, discard seeds, and chop. Place peppers in large bowl.

2  Add beans, corn, onion, lime juice, oil, chile powder, cumin, and salt and stir to combine. Serve chilled or at room temperature.

FYI  To bulk up this salad, you can add 1 cup of halved grape tomatoes and a peeled and chopped Kirby cucumber. If you have cilantro on hand, stir in 2 tablespoons chopped fresh cilantro just before serving.

# Lemony Wheat Berry, Zucchini, and Almond Salad

SERVES 4

▲ ³/₄ cup wheat berries

▲ 1 lemon, halved

▲ 2 medium zucchini, coarsely shredded

¼ cup lemon juice

1 tablespoon olive oil

½ teaspoon salt

½ teaspoon black pepper

¼ cup sliced almonds, toasted

PER SERVING (1¼ cups):
213 Cal, 7 g Total Fat, 1 g Sat Fat,
0 g Trans Fat, 0 mg Chol,
302 mg Sod, 31 g Carb, 3 g Sugar,
6 g Fib, 8 g Prot, 53 mg Calc.

5
PointsPlus®
value

1  Bring large pot of water to boil over medium-high heat; stir in wheat berries and lemon halves. Reduce heat and simmer, covered, until berries are tender but still chewy, 45 minutes–1 hour. Drain in colander and rinse under cold running water; drain again.

2  Discard lemon halves. Squeeze excess liquid from zucchini and place in large bowl; stir in wheat berries, lemon juice, oil, salt, and pepper. Stir in almonds just before serving. Serve chilled or at room temperature.

FYI  To make the salad more filling, you can add 1 cup of halved cherry tomatoes.

# Barley and Edamame Salad

SERVES 4

3 cups water

▲ ³/₄ cup pearl barley

▲ 2 cups shelled frozen edamame, thawed

▲ ¹/₃ cup finely shredded carrot

3 tablespoons rice vinegar

3 tablespoons reduced-sodium soy sauce

1¹/₂ tablespoons minced peeled fresh ginger

1 teaspoon Asian (dark) sesame oil

**PER SERVING (1 cup):**
219 Cal, 4 g Total Fat, 0 g Sat Fat, 0 g Trans Fat, 0 mg Chol, 421 mg Sod, 37 g Carb, 2 g Sugar, 9 g Fib, 11 g Prot, 57 mg Calc.

1  Bring water to boil in medium saucepan. Add barley. Reduce heat and simmer, covered, until barley is tender, about 25 minutes. Drain in colander and rinse under cold running water; drain again. Transfer to large bowl.

2  Add edamame, carrot, vinegar, soy sauce, ginger, and oil to barley and stir to combine. Serve chilled or at room temperature.

FYI  To add more color and crunch to this salad, you can add an English (seedless) cucumber, halved lengthwise and sliced.

QUINOA AND GRILLED
VEGETABLE SALAD

# Quinoa and Grilled Vegetable Salad

SERVES 4

▲ 1 cup red or white quinoa, rinsed

2 cups water

▲ 3 small zucchini, halved lengthwise

▲ 2 small fennel bulbs, trimmed and cut into ½-inch slices

▲ 2 small red onions, halved lengthwise

▲ 4 whole scallions

½ cup chopped fresh parsley

1½ tablespoons white balsamic vinegar

1 tablespoon olive oil

½ teaspoon salt

½ teaspoon black pepper

2 tablespoons pine nuts, toasted

PER SERVING (1½ cups):
283 Cal, 10 g Total Fat, 1 g Sat Fat,
0 g Trans Fat, 0 mg Chol,
367 mg Sod, 43 g Carb, 4 g Sugar,
8 g Fib, 9 g Prot, 107 mg Calc.

1 Combine quinoa and water in small saucepan; bring to boil. Reduce heat; cover and simmer until liquid is absorbed and quinoa is tender, about 12 minutes. Spoon quinoa onto large plate and let stand to cool.

2 Meanwhile, spray ridged grill pan with nonstick spray; set over medium-high heat until hot. Add zucchini, fennel, onion, and scallions in batches and cook, turning occasionally, until lightly browned and crisp-tender, about 5 minutes. Transfer vegetables to cutting board and coarsely chop.

3 Combine vegetables, quinoa, parsley, vinegar, oil, salt, and pepper in large bowl and stir to mix well. Stir in pine nuts just before serving. Serve chilled or at room temperature.

FYI White balsamic vinegar has a light, fruity flavor and is not as sweet as regular balsamic vinegar. Because of its pale color (it's made from white wine instead of red), you can use it in dishes where you don't want the dark color of regular balsamic vinegar.

# Quinoa and Spinach Salad

SERVES 4

▲ 1 cup quinoa, rinsed

2 cups water

¼ cup lime juice

2 teaspoons honey

1 tablespoon olive oil

½ teaspoon ground cumin

½ teaspoon salt

Pinch cayenne

▲ 1 mango, peeled, pitted, and cubed

▲ 1 red bell pepper, diced

▲ 2 scallions, thinly sliced

▲ 1 jalapeño pepper, seeded and minced

▲ ½ English (seedless) cucumber, peeled and diced

▲ 3 cups baby spinach

**PER SERVING (2 cups):**
259 Cal, 6 g Total Fat, 1 g Sat Fat,
0 g Trans Fat, 0 mg Chol,
331 mg Sod, 45 g Carb, 13 g Sugar,
6 g Fib, 7 g Prot, 58 mg Calc.

**1** Combine quinoa and water in small saucepan; bring to boil. Reduce heat; cover and simmer until liquid is absorbed and quinoa is tender, about 12 minutes. Spoon quinoa into large bowl and let stand to cool.

**2** Meanwhile, whisk together lime juice, honey, oil, cumin, salt, and cayenne in small bowl.

**3** Add lime mixture to quinoa; toss to coat. Add mango, bell pepper, scallions, jalapeño, and cucumber; toss to coat. Gently stir in spinach and serve at once.

**FYI** To make the salad up to a day ahead, leave out the spinach, and cover and refrigerate. Just before serving, add the spinach and toss gently to combine.

# Whole Grain– Vegetable Salad with Peanut Dressing

SERVES 4

- ▲ **1 cup brown rice**
- ▲ **1/2 cup pearl barley**
- **2 tablespoons creamy peanut butter**
- **2 tablespoons rice vinegar**
- **2 tablespoons reduced-sodium soy sauce**
- **2 tablespoons water**
- **1 tablespoon packed light brown sugar**
- **1 tablespoon Asian (dark) sesame oil**
- **2 garlic cloves, minced**
- **2 teaspoons minced peeled fresh ginger**
- **1/8 teaspoon cayenne**
- ▲ **2 assorted color bell peppers, diced**
- ▲ **1 small red onion, diced**
- ▲ **1 English (seedless) cucumber, peeled and diced**
- **1/2 cup chopped fresh cilantro**
- **2 tablespoons unsalted dry-roasted peanuts, chopped**

**PER SERVING** (1 1/2 cups salad and 1/2 tablespoon peanuts): 312 Cal, 11 g Total Fat, 2 g Sat Fat, 0 g Trans Fat, 0 mg Chol, 314 mg Sod, 49 g Carb, 8 g Sugar, 8 g Fib, 9 g Prot, 48 mg Calc.

**1**  Place brown rice and barley in large saucepan. Add enough water to cover by 2 inches and bring to boil. Reduce heat and simmer, covered, until rice mixture is tender, 30–40 minutes. Drain and place in large bowl. Let stand, stirring occasionally, until cool.

**2**  To make dressing, whisk together peanut butter, vinegar, soy sauce, water, sugar, sesame oil, garlic, ginger, and cayenne in small bowl.

**3**  Add bell peppers, onion, cucumber, and cilantro to rice mixture; toss to combine. Drizzle with dressing and toss to coat. Serve sprinkled with peanuts.

**FYI**  To turn this salad into a heartier main dish, you can add 8 ounces of small cooked shrimp. The per-serving *PointsPlus* value will increase by *1*.

# Tomato Tabbouleh

SERVES 4

▲ 1 cup bulgur

1 cup boiling water

▲ 2 cups grape tomatoes, halved

3/4 cup chopped fresh
flat-leaf parsley

▲ 1/2 English (seedless) cucumber,
peeled and diced

▲ 1/4 cup diced red onion

2 teaspoons grated lemon zest

2 tablespoons fresh lemon juice

1 tablespoon olive oil

1/2 teaspoon salt

1/2 teaspoon black pepper

1/4 cup crumbled reduced-fat
feta cheese

PER SERVING (about 3/4 cup):
195 Cal, 5 g Total Fat, 1 g Sat Fat,
0 g Trans Fat, 3 mg Chol,
428 mg Sod, 33 g Carb, 3 g Sugar,
8 g Fib, 7 g Prot, 71 mg Calc.

**1** Place bulgur in large bowl. Pour boiling water over bulgur and let stand until water is absorbed, about 30 minutes.

**2** Add tomatoes, parsley, cucumber, onion, lemon zest and juice, oil, salt, and pepper; toss well to coat. Sprinkle with feta just before serving.

**FYI** You can add more protein to this salad by tossing in a 15 1/2-ounce can chickpeas, rinsed and drained. The per-serving *PointsPlus* value will increase by *3*.

# Kasha Varnishkes Soup

SERVES 4

1 tablespoon unsalted butter

▲ 2 onions, chopped

▲ 8 cups reduced-sodium vegetable broth

▲ ½ cup kasha

½ teaspoon salt

½ teaspoon black pepper

▲ 4 ounces whole wheat bow-tie pasta

▲ 1 carrot, diced

**PER SERVING (2¼ cups):**
262 Cal, 4 g Total Fat, 2 g Sat Fat,
0 g Trans Fat, 8 mg Chol,
592 mg Sod, 50 g Carb, 10 g Sugar,
9 g Fib, 7 g Prot, 81 mg Calc.

1  Heat butter in Dutch oven over medium-low heat. Add onion; cook, stirring often, until onion is golden, 15 minutes.

2  Add broth, kasha, salt, and pepper; bring to boil. Reduce heat, cover, and simmer 8 minutes.

3  Stir in pasta and carrot. Partially cover and simmer until kasha and pasta are tender, 12 minutes.

**FYI**  Kasha is roasted hulled buckwheat grains. It has a toasty nutty flavor and can be used to make hot cereal, pilaf, or varnishkes, a dish made with kasha and bow-tie pasta. To put even more veggies in this nourishing soup, add 3 celery stalks, chopped, with the carrot in step 3 and stir in 2 cups baby spinach during the last minute of cooking.

# Wheat Berry and Apple Salad

SERVES 6

▲ 1 cup wheat berries

2 tablespoons white wine vinegar

2 tablespoons unsweetened apple juice

1 tablespoon olive oil

1 tablespoon minced peeled fresh ginger

1/4 teaspoon salt

▲ 2 Gala apples, cored and cut into 1-inch chunks

▲ 2 celery stalks, thinly sliced

▲ 1 small red onion, sliced

1/2 cup raisins

1/4 cup chopped almonds, toasted

1/4 cup chopped fresh flat-leaf parsley

Lemon wedges

**PER SERVING** (about 1 cup):
254 Cal, 6 g Total Fat, 1 g Sat Fat,
0 g Trans Fat, 0 mg Chol,
123 mg Sod, 45 g Carb, 18 g Sugar,
7 g Fib, 7 g Prot, 53 mg Calc.

1  Bring large pot of water to boil over medium-high heat; stir in wheat berries. Reduce heat and simmer, covered, until berries are tender but still chewy, 45 minutes–1 hour. Drain in colander and rinse under cold running water; drain again.

2  Whisk together vinegar, apple juice, oil, ginger, and salt in large bowl. Add wheat berries, apples, celery, onion, raisins, almonds, and parsley and toss to combine. Serve with lemon wedges.

**FYI** If you'd like to add more fresh fruit to this salad, toss in a cored and diced pear.

**WHEAT BERRY AND APPLE SALAD**

# Coconut Creamed Corn

▲ 1 onion, chopped

2 garlic cloves, minced

▲ 2 cups fresh corn kernels or frozen corn, thawed

▲ 1 (15-ounce) can hominy, rinsed and drained

⅓ cup light (reduced-fat) coconut milk

▲ ¼ cup reduced-sodium vegetable broth

½ teaspoon red pepper flakes

¼ teaspoon salt

¼ cup chopped fresh cilantro

1 tablespoon lime juice

**PER SERVING (¾ cup):**
173 Cal, 3 g Total Fat, 0 g Sat Fat,
0 g Trans Fat, 0 mg Chol,
391 mg Sod, 35 g Carb, 7 g Sugar,
6 g Fib, 5 g Prot, 27 mg Calc.

**1**  Spray large nonstick skillet with nonstick spray; set over medium heat. Add onion and garlic and cook, stirring often, until onion is softened, 5 minutes.

**2**  Add corn, hominy, coconut milk, broth, pepper flakes, and salt and bring to boil. Reduce heat, partially cover, and simmer until corn is tender 8–10 minutes. Remove from heat and stir in cilantro and lime juice.

# Spicy Corn Soufflé

SERVES 4

▲ 1 (16-ounce) tube refrigerated fat-free plain polenta, cut into 2-inch pieces

▲ ½ cup fat-free milk

▲ ¾ cup frozen corn kernels, thawed

½ cup shredded reduced-fat Mexican cheese blend

▲ ¼ cup canned diced chiles

2 egg yolks

2 tablespoons chopped fresh cilantro

¼ teaspoon salt

▲ 3 egg whites

**PER SERVING** (¼ of soufflé): 200 Cal, 6 g Total Fat, 2 g Sat Fat, 0 g Trans Fat, 115 mg Chol, 689 mg Sod, 26 g Carb, 3 g Sugar, 2 g Fib, 12 g Prot, 179 mg Calc.

1  Preheat oven to 375°F. Spray 2-quart round baking dish with nonstick spray.

2  Place polenta and milk in food processor; process until smooth. Transfer polenta mixture to large bowl. Stir in corn, cheese, chiles, egg yolks, cilantro, and salt.

3  With electric mixer on high speed, beat egg whites in medium bowl until soft peaks form. Stir one fourth of egg whites into polenta mixture to lighten. Gently fold in remaining egg whites just until no streaks of white remain. Spoon into baking dish.

4  Bake until puffed and golden, about 45 minutes. Serve at once.

**FYI**  You can serve the soufflé as a light lunch if you accompany it with a salad. To do so, toss together mixed baby greens, halved cherry tomatoes, and thinly sliced red onion and cucumber. Add lime juice and salt and pepper to taste and toss to combine.

# Amaranth "Polenta" with Baby Leeks and Shiitakes

SERVES 6

1 tablespoon unsalted butter

▲ 6 ounces shiitake mushrooms, stems removed, and caps sliced

▲ 6 baby leeks, thinly sliced (white and light green parts only)

▲ 2 ¼ cups reduced-sodium vegetable broth

▲ 1½ cups amaranth

1 tablespoon minced fresh thyme

½ teaspoon salt

½ teaspoon black pepper

3 tablespoons grated Parmesan cheese

PER SERVING (½ cup):
239 Cal, 6 g Total Fat, 3 g Sat Fat,
0 g Trans Fat, 7 mg Chol,
291 mg Sod, 39 g Carb, 3 g Sugar,
5 g Fib, 8 g Prot, 126 mg Calc.

6 PointsPlus® value

1 Heat butter in a medium skillet over medium heat. Add mushrooms and leeks and cook, stirring often, until vegetables are softened, 5 minutes. Set aside.

2 Combine broth, amaranth, thyme, salt, and pepper in a medium saucepan, bring to boil. Reduce heat, cover, and simmer 30 minutes, stirring often, until amaranth is tender. Serve topped with reserved mushroom mixture and sprinkled with Parmesan.

FYI To serve additional leeks with the amaranth, spray large nonstick skillet with nonstick spray and set over medium heat. Add leeks and cook turning ocassionally until lightly browned, about 6 minutes. Add a few tablespoons of water, cover, and steam until tender, 5 minutes longer.

# Wild Rice with Apricots and Pecans

▲ **1 cup wild rice**

**2 teaspoons grated orange zest**

**¼ cup orange juice**

**1 teaspoon honey**

**¼ teaspoon salt**

**⅛ teaspoon black pepper**

▲ **2 scallions, thinly sliced**

**½ cup dried apricots, thinly sliced**

**3 tablespoons coarsely chopped pecans**

**1 tablespoon chopped fresh thyme**

**PER SERVING** (about ⅔ cup):
166 Cal, 3 g Total Fat, 0 g Sat Fat,
0 g Trans Fat, 0 mg Chol,
101 mg Sod, 32 g Carb, 8 g Sugar,
3 g Fib, 5 g Prot, 16 mg Calc.

**1** Cook rice according to package directions; drain.

**2** Meanwhile, whisk together orange zest and juice, honey, salt, and pepper in large bowl. Add rice, scallions, apricots, pecans, and thyme and toss to combine. Serve hot or at room temperature.

**FYI** Why not add a cored and thinly sliced apple or pear to give this side dish bright color and tart, fresh flavor?

WILD RICE WITH APRICOTS
AND PECANS

# North African Bulgur Pilaf

SERVES 6

1 tablespoon unsalted butter

▲ 1 small onion, chopped

1 garlic clove, minced

1 teaspoon ground cinnamon

1 teaspoon ground coriander

1 teaspoon ground cumin

1 teaspoon ground ginger

½ teaspoon salt

½ teaspoon black pepper

▲ 2 cups reduced-sodium vegetable broth

▲ 2 cups medium-coarse, quick-cooking bulgur

16 dried apricots, quartered

2 tablespoons sliced almonds, toasted

**PER SERVING (1 cup):**
225 Cal, 4 g Total Fat, 1 g Sat Fat, 0 g Trans Fat, 5 mg Chol, 251 mg Sod, 45 g Carb, 6 g Sugar, 10 g Fib, 7 g Prot, 46 mg Calc.

1  Heat butter in large saucepan over medium heat. Add onion and garlic and cook, stirring often, until onion is softened, 5 minutes. Add cinnamon, coriander, cumin, ginger, salt, and pepper and cook, stirring constantly, until fragrant, 30 seconds.

2  Add broth and bring to boil. Stir in bulgur and apricots. Remove from heat, cover, and let stand until broth is absorbed, about 30 minutes. Fluff bulgur with a fork and stir in almonds.

**FYI**  This aromatic pilaf makes the perfect accompaniment with roasted or grilled chicken. A 3-ounce portion of cooked skinless boneless chicken breast per serving will increase the *PointsPlus* value by *3*.

# Quinoa and Mushroom Pilaf

SERVES 6

2 teaspoons olive oil

▲ 4 ounces shiitake mushrooms, stems removed and caps sliced

2 garlic cloves, minced

1 shallot, minced

▲ 1 cup quinoa, rinsed

▲ 2 cups reduced-sodium chicken broth

¹/₄ teaspoon salt

¹/₈ teaspoon black pepper

2 tablespoons chopped fresh flat-leaf parsley

**PER SERVING (²/₃ cup):**
147 Cal, 4 g Total Fat, 1 g Sat Fat,
0 g Trans Fat, 0 mg Chol,
125 mg Sod, 23 g Carb, 1 g Sugar,
2 g Fib, 6 g Prot, 23 mg Calc.

1  Heat oil in a large skillet over medium heat. Add mushrooms, garlic, and shallot; cook, stirring occasionally, until mushrooms are tender, about 5 minutes.

2  Stir in quinoa, broth, salt, and pepper; bring to boil. Reduce heat and simmer, covered, until all liquid is absorbed, 15–20 minutes. Remove from heat and stir in parsley.

**FYI** You can use any kind of mushrooms to make this dish. Try cremini, oyster, or white mushrooms, or a mixture of each.

SPICY BLACK-EYED PEA
CORNBREAD

# Spicy Black-Eyed Pea Cornbread

SERVES 10

1 cup yellow cornmeal
1 cup whole wheat flour
1½ teaspoons baking powder
1 teaspoon salt
1 large egg
1 cup low-fat buttermilk
2 tablespoons sugar
▲ 1 (10-ounce) can diced tomatoes with chiles, drained
▲ 1 cup canned black-eyed peas, rinsed and drained
▲ 1 small green bell pepper, diced

**PER SERVING (1 wedge):**
144 Cal, 1 g Total Fat, 1 g Sat Fat,
0 g Trans Fat, 20 mg Chol,
422 mg Sod, 29 g Carb, 5 g Sugar,
4 g Fib, 5 g Prot, 78 mg Calc.

1 Preheat oven to 375°F. Spray 10-inch cast-iron or other heavy ovenproof skillet with nonstick spray.

2 Whisk together cornmeal, flour, baking powder, and salt in large bowl. Whisk together egg, buttermilk, and sugar in small bowl. Add egg mixture, tomatoes, black-eyed peas, and bell pepper to cornmeal mixture and stir just until flour is moistened.

3 Pour batter into skillet and bake until top is lightly browned and firm to the touch, about 25 minutes. Let cool on wire rack 5 minutes. Cut into 10 wedges. Serve warm.

**FYI** You can add more color and flavor by adding ½ cup thinly sliced scallions along with the bell pepper in step 2.

# Multigrain Banana Bread

SERVES 12

½ cup plus 2 tablespoons all-purpose flour

½ cup whole wheat pastry flour

¼ cup oat bran

¼ cup yellow cornmeal

½ teaspoon ground cinnamon

½ teaspoon baking powder

½ teaspoon baking soda

½ teaspoon salt

▲ 3 large egg whites

½ cup packed dark brown sugar

¼ cup canola oil

▲ 3 ripe bananas, peeled and mashed

½ teaspoon almond extract

**PER SERVING (1 slice):**
141 Cal, 1 g Total Fat, 0 g Sat Fat, 0 g Trans Fat, 0 mg Chol, 189 mg Sod, 32 g Carb, 13 g Sugar, 2 g Fib, 4 g Prot, 20 mg Calc.

**1** Preheat oven to 350°F. Spray 5 x 9-inch loaf pan with nonstick spray.

**2** Whisk together flours, oat bran, cornmeal, cinnamon, baking powder, baking soda, and salt in medium bowl. Set aside.

**3** With electric mixer on medium speed, beat egg whites, sugar, and oil in large bowl until creamy, about 3 minutes. Beat in bananas and almond extract. Reduce speed to low; beat flour mixture into banana mixture until just combined.

**4** Pour batter into pan and bake until toothpick inserted into center of loaf comes out clean, 45–50 minutes. Cool in pan 10 minutes. Remove bread from pan and cool completely on wire rack. Cut into 12 slices.

**FYI** Whole wheat pastry flour is a great addition to your healthy pantry. It's very finely ground so you can use it to create cakes and muffins with a light and delicate texture.

# Spelt Noodle and Pear Kugel

SERVES 6

▲ 8 ounces spelt noodles

▲ 2 large eggs, at room temperature

▲ 1/2 cup fat-free sour cream

1/3 cup low-fat (1%) milk

3 tablespoons honey

1 teaspoon vanilla extract

1/4 teaspoon ground cinnamon

▲ 1 pear, peeled, cored, and chopped

**PER SERVING** (1 1/4 cups):
224 Cal, 3 g Total Fat, 1 g Sat Fat,
0 g Trans Fat, 74 mg Chol,
59 mg Sod, 45 g Carb, 15 g Sugar,
5 g Fib, 9 g Prot, 54 mg Calc.

1  Cook noodles according to package directions omitting salt, if desired; drain. Rinse under cold running water; drain.

2  Preheat oven to 350°F. Spray 1½-quart baking dish or soufflé dish with nonstick spray.

3  Whisk together eggs, sour cream, milk, honey, vanilla, and cinnamon in large bowl until smooth. Stir in pear and noodles. Pour into baking dish.

4  Bake until top is golden brown, 45 minutes. Let stand 10 minutes before serving. Serve warm.

**FYI**  Spelt is an ancient grain native to southern Europe. It has a mild, nutty flavor and contains more protein than wheat.

**2 cups water**

▲ **½ cup pearl barley**

**2 cups low-fat (1%) milk**

**¼ cup sugar**

**¼ cup raisins**

**¼ teaspoon ground cinnamon**

▲ **1 large egg, at room temperature**

▲ **1 large egg white, at room temperature**

**1 teaspoon vanilla extract**

**PER SERVING (generous ½ cup):**
227 Cal, 3 g Total Fat, 1 g Sat Fat,
0 g Trans Fat, 60 mg Chol,
93 mg Sod, 43 g Carb, 23 g Sugar,
4 g Fib, 9 g Prot, 168 mg Calc.

# Cinnamon-Raisin Barley Pudding

**1** Bring water to boil in large saucepan. Add barley. Reduce heat and simmer, covered, until barley is tender, about 25 minutes. Drain.

**2** Return barley to saucepan; add milk, sugar, raisins, and cinnamon and bring to simmer over medium heat. Reduce heat to low and simmer, stirring occasionally, until mixture is thickened, about 1 hour.

**3** Whisk together egg, egg white, and vanilla in medium bowl. Whisk about half of hot barley mixture into egg mixture. Return barley mixture to saucepan and cook, whisking constantly, over low heat until pudding is very thick, about 2 minutes. Serve warm.

**FYI** Instead of raisins, you can make this creamy pudding with chopped dried apricots, apples, or pears. Sprinkle the pudding with freshly grated nutmeg and serve with a handful of fresh cherries.

**CINNAMON-RAISIN
BARLEY PUDDING**

SPELT CRÊPES WITH
FRUIT AND HONEY

# Spelt Crêpes with Fruit and Honey

SERVES 2

UNDER 20 MINUTES

½ cup low-fat (1%) milk

▲ 1 large egg white

2 teaspoons unsalted butter, melted

½ teaspoon vanilla extract

¼ teaspoon salt

½ cup spelt flour

▲ 1 cup fresh blueberries

▲ 1 large nectarine, pitted and thinly sliced

2 teaspoons honey

1 teaspoon confectioners' sugar

**PER SERVING** (2 filled crêpes, and 1 teaspoon honey): 260 Cal, 9 g Total Fat, 5 g Sat Fat, 0 g Trans Fat, 23 mg Chol, 347 mg Sod, 37 g Carb, 13 g Sugar, 6 g Fib, 9 g Prot, 92 mg Calc.

7 PointsPlus® value

1  Whisk together milk, egg white, butter, vanilla, and salt in large bowl. Add flour and whisk until smooth.

2  Spray large nonstick skillet with nonstick spray and set over medium heat. When a drop of water sizzles in pan, pour ¼ cup batter into skillet, and swirl to make thin, circular layer of batter. Cook until underside is set, 1–2 minutes. Flip and cook through, about 15 seconds longer. Transfer to wire rack. Repeat with remaining batter, making a total of 4 crêpes.

3  Fold each crêpe into quarters and place 2 crêpes on each of 2 serving plates; tuck blueberries and nectarine slices inside the crêpes. Drizzle evenly with honey and sprinkle with confectioners' sugar.

**FYI**  To add even more fruit, you can serve the crêpes with a cup of raspberries in addition to the blueberries.

# Vegetables

Soups, Salads, and Sides

# Vegetables

## YOU NEED

5 servings of fruits and vegetables per day; 9 servings if you weigh more than 350 pounds. A serving of leafy greens is 1 cup; for other vegetables a serving is ½ cup.

## WHY THEY'RE ESSENTIAL

**Most vegetables have a *0 PointsPlus* value.** With the ***PointsPlus*** plan, almost all vegetables, (with the exception of starchy vegetables such as corn, peas, and potatoes) are free, which means you don't have to count their ***PointsPlus*** value. Keep in mind that only plain vegetables are free. If you add ingredients such as oil, butter, cheese, or breadcrumbs, you have to take into account the ***PointsPlus*** values of those ingredients and the vegetables.

**Fill up on fiber.** Vegetables are an excellent source of fiber, which slows down digestion and the rate at which sugars are absorbed into the blood. You need 25 to 35 grams of fiber each day, but only half of Americans get the recommended amount. The best vegetable sources for fiber are artichokes, broccoli, peas, spinach, sweet potatoes, and acorn squash.

**Vegetables protect your health.** People who regularly consume vegetables have a reduced risk of developing heart disease, diabetes, and certain cancers.

## WHAT TO BUY

**Fresh vegetables:** In warm months, shop at a local farmers' market whenever possible for the freshest and best-tasting vegetables. At other times, shop at a busy supermarket with a well-stocked produce section for a diverse garden-fresh selection of vegetables.

**Frozen vegetables:** Buy plain frozen vegetables without added sauces or seasonings. Frozen vegetables have virtually the same nutrient content as fresh.

*TIP: Individually quick-frozen vegetables that come in plastic bags make it easy to cook one or two servings at a time.*

**Canned vegetables:** Look for plain canned vegetables without added seasonings.

*TIP: Always choose a no-salt-added or reduced-sodium variety when possible.*

## GOOD TO KNOW

**Vitamins don't replace veggies.** Even if you take a multivitamin every day, it's important to still eat at least 5 servings of fruits and vegetables each day. Whole foods contain fiber, phytochemicals, and antioxidants that help protect your health.

**Variety is the key.** Different vegetables contain different types of vitamins, minerals, and phytochemicals, and different amounts of fiber. Eat a varied combination of vegetables every day, including leafy greens and colorful vegetables to ensure that you get adequate nutrient and fiber intake.

## Lettuce and leafy greens

### POWER-UP IDEAS

- Buy prewashed salad greens or wash a big batch at home to make it effortless to have a salad with dinner every day.

- Have a side salad instead of French fries when you eat fast food.

- Sturdy greens such as Swiss chard or kale are delicious when simply steamed or, if thinly sliced, they can be enjoyed raw.

### TAKE NOTE

- Greens, such as spinach, mustard, turnip, kale, and collards, are excellent sources of vitamin A.

- Peppery-tasting arugula is an excellent source of vitamin K, which is essential for bone health.

- Salad greens such as romaine, red and green leaf lettuce, and Bibb lettuce are all good sources of vitamins A and K and the antioxidant lutein, which is good for eye health.

## Green vegetables

such as artichokes, asparagus, broccoli, Brussels sprouts, and green beans

### POWER-UP IDEAS

- Start early in the day by adding diced bell peppers, summer squash, or onions to omelets, frittatas, or scrambled eggs.

- Make canned soup healthier. Add a cup of quick-cooking small broccoli florets, chopped zucchini, or baby spinach when you heat the soup.

- When eating pizza, sandwiches, pasta dishes, or stir-fries in a restaurant, choose options with the most veggies.

### TAKE NOTE

- Asparagus is one of the best vegetable sources of folate.

- Broccoli has one of the highest amounts of calcium found in any vegetable and also contains phytochemicals that can protect against cancer.

- Green beans are a great vegetable source of fiber, vitamin C, and vitamin K.

## Colorful vegetables

such as beets, carrots, tomatoes, and winter squash

### POWER-UP IDEAS

- Craving crunch? Opt for cut up carrots, celery, radishes, or jicama instead of chips or crackers.

- Double up. Instead of a single vegetable at dinner, eat two.

- Use the microwave to make quick work of preparing long-cooking vegetables such as winter squash or beets.

### TAKE NOTE

- Red and green peppers and tomatoes are good sources of vitamin C.

- Just one medium carrot contains more than twice the amount of vitamin A you need in a day.

- Eggplant, especially the peel, contains a powerful phytonutrient, which may prevent free radical formation that can damage cells.

# Vegetable and Farro Soup with Gremolata

SERVES 6

▲ ½ cup farro

2 teaspoons olive oil

▲ 1 large onion, chopped

5 garlic cloves, finely minced

▲ 2 large carrots, sliced

▲ 2 large celery stalks with leaves, sliced

▲ 1 leek, halved lengthwise and sliced (white and light green parts only)

▲ ½ small head green cabbage, coarsely chopped (2 cups)

1 teaspoon dried thyme

½ teaspoon dried rosemary

¼ teaspoon black pepper

▲ 6 cups reduced-sodium vegetable broth

1 cup chopped fresh flat-leaf parsley

1 tablespoon grated lemon zest

**PER SERVING (1½ cups):**
149 Cal, 2 g Total Fat, 0 g Sat Fat,
0 g Trans Fat, 0 mg Chol,
215 mg Sod, 28 g Carb, 8 g Sugar,
6 g Fib, 5 g Prot, 131 mg Calc.

**4**
PointsPlus©
value

**1**  Combine farro and enough water to cover in medium bowl. Let stand 30 minutes. Drain.

**2**  Heat oil in Dutch oven over medium heat. Add onion and 4 garlic cloves  and cook, stirring occasionally, until softened, 5 minutes. Add carrots, celery, leek, cabbage, thyme, rosemary, pepper, and 2 tablespoons broth. Cover and cook, stirring occasionally, until vegetables are softened, 10 minutes.

**3**  Add remaining broth and farro; bring to boil. Reduce heat and simmer, covered, until farro and vegetables are very tender, about 30 minutes.

**4**  To make gremolata, stir together parsley, lemon zest, and remaining garlic clove in small bowl. Stir into soup and serve at once.

**FYI**  Farro is a type of wheat similar to wheat berries. Look for it in Italian markets or natural foods stores. If you can't find it, you can substitute wheat berries or barley in this hearty main dish recipe. To make the soup more filling, add 1½ cups frozen baby lima beans to the soup during the last 8 minutes of cooking (the per-serving *PointsPlus* value will increase by *1*).

**VEGETABLE AND FARRO SOUP WITH GREMOLATA**

# Escarole Soup with Spelt Orzo

**SERVES 4**

▲ ⅓ cup spelt orzo

1 tablespoon olive oil

▲ 1 large onion, chopped

▲ 1 large carrot, chopped

4 garlic cloves, minced

3 tablespoons chopped fresh sage

¼ teaspoon salt

⅛ teaspoon black pepper

▲ 1 medium head escarole, coarsely chopped (about 10 cups)

▲ 3 cups reduced-sodium vegetable broth

▲ 1 pound plum tomatoes, coarsely chopped (1¾ cups)

1 cup water

4 tablespoons grated Pecorino or Parmesan cheese

**PER SERVING (1¾ cups):**
199 Cal, 6 g Total Fat, 1 g Sat Fat, 0 g Trans Fat, 4 mg Chol, 378 mg Sod, 29 g Carb, 7 g Sugar, 10 g Fib, 8 g Prot, 193 mg Calc.

**5** PointsPlus® value

**1**  Cook orzo according to package directions, omitting salt, if desired. Drain.

**2**  Meanwhile, heat oil in Dutch oven over medium heat. Add onion, carrot, and garlic and cook, stirring often, until vegetables are lightly browned, about 8 minutes. Stir in sage, salt, and pepper.

**3**  Add half of escarole and 1 tablespoon broth. Cook, stirring frequently, until escarole is wilted, about 2 minutes. Repeat with remaining escarole and another 1 tablespoon broth. Add remaining broth, tomatoes, and water; bring to boil. Reduce heat and simmer, covered, until escarole is tender, 10 minutes.

**4**  Stir in orzo and cook until heated through, about 2 minutes. Ladle soup evenly into 4 serving bowls; sprinkle with Pecorino.

**FYI**  Spelt pastas are made with whole grain spelt, which is related to wheat. Spelt retains more of the nutrients of the original ancient wheat grain. It's a good source of riboflavin, manganese, and niacin. If it's not available, you can use whole wheat orzo in this recipe.

# Herbed Asparagus and Fingerling Potato Soup

SERVES 4

1 tablespoon olive oil

▲ 1 large onion, chopped

▲ 1 celery stalk, thinly sliced

2 garlic cloves, minced

2 tablespoons chopped fresh thyme

¼ teaspoon salt

⅛ teaspoon black pepper

▲ 2 cups reduced-sodium vegetable broth

2 cups water

▲ ¾ pound fingerling or other small potatoes, scrubbed and thinly sliced

▲ 1 pound asparagus, trimmed

1 tablespoon chopped fresh tarragon

▲ 4 tablespoons plain fat-free Greek yogurt

**1** Heat oil in Dutch oven over medium heat. Add onion, celery, and garlic and cook, stirring often, until vegetables are softened, 5 minutes. Stir in thyme, salt, and pepper. Add broth, water, and potatoes; bring to boil. Reduce heat and simmer, covered, until potatoes are almost tender, about 8 minutes.

**2** Meanwhile, cut tips of asparagus into 1-inch pieces and thinly slice stalks. Add asparagus to soup and simmer, covered, until tender, about 5 minutes longer. Stir in tarragon. Ladle soup evenly into 4 serving bowls; top with yogurt.

**FYI** Fingerling potatoes make attractive small round slices for this soup, but if they aren't available, use small white potatoes. You can also make the soup with regular large potatoes, cutting them into quarters before slicing.

PER SERVING (1½ cups soup with 1 tablespoon yogurt):
148 Cal, 4 g Total Fat, 1 g Sat Fat, 0 g Trans Fat, 0 mg Chol, 249 mg Sod, 25 g Carb, 6 g Sugar, 5 g Fib, 6 g Prot, 83 mg Calc.

**4** PointsPlus© value

# Roasted Tomato Broth with Crispy Tortillas

**SERVES 4**

▲ 1½ pounds plum tomatoes, halved and cored

▲ 1 large sweet onion, cut into thick slices

▲ 1 red bell pepper, sliced

4 teaspoons olive oil

3 garlic cloves, minced

1 teaspoon chili powder

½ teaspoon dried oregano

¼ teaspoon red pepper flakes

⅛ teaspoon salt

2 (8-inch) whole wheat tortillas, halved and thinly sliced

½ teaspoon ground cumin

▲ 2 cups reduced-sodium vegetable broth

½ avocado, peeled, pitted, and diced

PER SERVING (1 cup soup, ¼ cup tortilla strips, and 2 tablespoons avocado): 177 Cal, 9 g Total Fat, 1 g Sat Fat, 0 g Trans Fat, 0 mg Chol, 368 mg Sod, 22 g Carb, 9 g Sugar, 9 g Fib, 7 g Prot, 72 mg Calc.

**1** Preheat oven to 425°F. Spray large rimmed baking pan and medium baking pan with nonstick spray.

**2** Place tomatoes, onion, and bell pepper in large pan. Drizzle with 2 teaspoons oil; sprinkle with garlic, chili powder, oregano, pepper flakes, and salt. Toss to coat.

**3** Arrange tomatoes on one side of pan, cut side down. Arrange onion and pepper on other side of pan in single layer. Roast, stirring onion and pepper occasionally, until vegetables are lightly browned and tender, about 25 minutes. Do not turn tomatoes. Remove from oven and let stand until cool enough to handle. Maintain oven temperature.

**4** Meanwhile, place tortilla strips in medium pan in single layer. Drizzle with remaining 2 teaspoons oil and cumin; toss to coat. Bake, stirring once, until lightly golden, about 6 minutes. Transfer to plate to cool.

**5** Remove and discard skins from tomatoes and chop pulp. Place pulp in large saucepan. Chop roasted onions and peppers and add to saucepan with any accumulated juices. Add broth; bring to boil over high heat, mashing vegetables with back of wooden spoon. Reduce heat and simmer, uncovered, 10 minutes. Ladle soup evenly into 4 serving bowls; top with tortilla strips and avocado.

**FYI** To add more protein and fiber to the soup, you can add 1 cup canned black beans, rinsed and drained, when you add the broth (¼ cup black beans per-serving will increase the *PointsPlus* value by *1*).

# Hot-and-Sour Mushroom Soup

SERVES 6

UNDER 20 MINUTES

▲ 5 cups reduced-sodium chicken broth

2 tablespoons cornstarch

1 tablespoon reduced-sodium soy sauce

▲ 1 pound mixed mushrooms, thinly sliced

3 tablespoons apple-cider vinegar

1 tablespoon minced peeled fresh ginger

2 teaspoons Asian (dark) sesame oil

3/4 teaspoon black pepper

▲ 3 large egg whites, lightly beaten

1/2 cup chopped fresh cilantro

**PER SERVING (about 1 1/2 cups):**
90 Cal, 3 g Total Fat, 1 g Sat Fat,
0 g Trans Fat, 0 mg Chol,
181 mg Sod, 10 g Carb, 2 g Sugar,
1 g Fib, 8 g Prot, 25 mg Calc.

**3** PointsPlus value

**1** Stir together 2 tablespoons broth and cornstarch in small cup until smooth.

**2** Bring remaining broth and soy sauce to boil over high heat in large pot. Add mushrooms; return to boil. Reduce heat and simmer until mushrooms are just tender, 3 minutes.

**3** Add cornstarch mixture and cook, stirring constantly, until soup thickens slightly, about 30 seconds. Stir in vinegar, ginger, sesame oil, and pepper.

**4** Remove pot from heat and add egg whites in slow, steady stream, stirring constantly. Ladle soup evenly into 6 soup bowls and serve sprinkled with cilantro.

**FYI** For an additional serving of healthful greens, you can add 2 cups chopped fresh spinach to the soup during the last minute of cooking the mushrooms in step 2.

# Quick Gazpacho

SERVES 6

▲ 2 (14 ½-ounce) cans petite diced tomatoes

2 cups reduced-sodium tomato-vegetable juice

▲ 1 red bell pepper, diced

▲ 1 English (seedless) cucumber, diced

▲ 1 jalapeño pepper, seeded and minced

▲ 1 small red onion, minced

1 tablespoon balsamic vinegar

¼ teaspoon salt

PER SERVING (1½ cups):
68 Cal, 0 g Total Fat, 0 g Sat Fat,
0 g Trans Fat, 0 mg Chol,
461 mg Sod, 14 g Carb, 10 g Sugar,
3 g Fib, 2 g Prot, 45 mg Calc.

Stir together all ingredients in large bowl. Refrigerate, covered, until chilled, about 4 hours.

**FYI** To make this soup a main dish and more filling, you can add 12 ounces small cooked shrimp. The per-serving *PointsPlus* value will increase by *1*.

# Greek Village Salad with Tzatziki Dressing

SERVES 4

UNDER 20 MINUTES

▲ ½ cup plain fat-free Greek yogurt

▲ ¼ cup finely chopped peeled cucumber

2 tablespoons chopped fresh mint

1 tablespoon olive oil

1 tablespoon lemon juice

1 small garlic clove, minced

¼ teaspoon dried oregano

¼ teaspoon salt

⅛ teaspoon black pepper

▲ 4 cups mixed salad greens

▲ 1 (15½-ounce) can cannellini (white kidney) beans, rinsed and drained

▲ 1 large tomato, cut into ½-inch pieces

▲ 1 small English (seedless) cucumber, halved lengthwise and sliced

▲ ¼ cup thinly sliced red onion

½ cup crumbled reduced-fat feta cheese

PER SERVING (2¼ cups salad with scant ¼ cup dressing): 203 Cal, 6 g Total Fat, 2 g Sat Fat, 0 g Trans Fat, 5 mg Chol, 702 mg Sod, 25 g Carb, 6 g Sugar, 8 g Fib, 14 g Prot, 137 mg Calc.

**1**  To make dressing, whisk together yogurt, chopped cucumber, mint, oil, lemon juice, garlic, oregano, salt, and pepper in small bowl.

**2**  Arrange greens on large platter. Top with beans, tomato, sliced cucumber, and onion. Spoon dressing evenly over salad and sprinkle with feta. Serve at once.

**FYI**  Tzatziki (pronounced dzah-DZEE-kee) is a classic Greek appetizer usually served along with other small dishes and with warmed pita bread. The refreshing cucumber and yogurt make it a fitting condiment for grilled fish or lamb, or as in this recipe, a crisp salad.

# Warm Spinach and Apple Salad with Curry Dressing

SERVES 4

UNDER 20 MINUTES

▲ 1 medium red onion, halved and thinly sliced

1 teaspoon packed light brown sugar

1 teaspoon curry powder

¹⁄₄ teaspoon salt

¹⁄₈ teaspoon black pepper

▲ ¹⁄₄ cup reduced-sodium vegetable broth

2 tablespoons balsamic vinegar

1 tablespoon olive oil

▲ 1 (6-ounce) package baby spinach

▲ 1 red apple, cored and sliced

PER SERVING (1¹⁄₄ cups):
98 Cal, 4 g Total Fat, 1 g Sat Fat,
0 g Trans Fat, 0 mg Chol,
226 mg Sod, 16 g Carb, 8 g Sugar,
4 g Fib, 2 g Prot, 46 mg Calc.

**1** Spray large nonstick skillet with nonstick spray and set over medium heat. Add onion and cook, stirring frequently, until softened, 5 minutes. Add brown sugar and stir to coat. Reduce heat and cook, stirring often, until onion is lightly browned, about 6 minutes.

**2** Add curry powder, salt, and pepper and cook, stirring constantly, 1 minute. Add broth, vinegar, and oil; bring to boil, stirring constantly.

**3** Combine spinach and apple in large bowl. Pour onion mixture over salad and toss to coat. Serve at once.

**FYI** For even more fresh fruit, add a ripe pear, cored and sliced, to the salad.

# Shredded Vegetable Salad with Poppy Seed Dressing

**SERVES 4**

**UNDER 20 MINUTES**

3 tablespoons low-fat buttermilk

2 tablespoons reduced-fat mayonnaise

2 teaspoons red-wine vinegar

½ teaspoon packed light brown sugar

1 teaspoon poppy seeds

1 teaspoon grated orange zest

¼ teaspoon salt

▲ 4 cups torn Bibb lettuce leaves

▲ 1 medium beet, peeled and coarsely shredded

▲ 1 large carrot, shredded

▲ 1 cup shredded zucchini

▲ 1 cup shredded cucumber

**PER SERVING** (2¼ cups salad with generous 1 tablespoon dressing): 56 Cal, 2 g Total Fat, 0 g Sat Fat, 0 g Trans Fat, 0 mg Chol, 257 mg Sod, 9 g Carb, 5 g Sugar, 2 g Fib, 2 g Prot, 62 mg Calc.

**1** To make dressing, whisk together buttermilk, mayonnaise, vinegar, brown sugar, poppy seeds, orange zest, and salt in small bowl.

**2** Divide lettuce evenly among 4 serving plates. Arrange shredded vegetables evenly in separate mounds on lettuce. Drizzle salads evenly with dressing and serve at once.

**FYI** The easiest way to shred vegetables is with the shredding attachment on your food processor. To avoid color bleeding, shred the cucumber and zucchini first, then the carrot, followed by the beet. Make sure to cut them into pieces that fit in the feed tube of the processor before shredding. You can also shred the vegetables using a box grater.

# Citrusy Carrot Salad with Green Olives

SERVES 4

2 tablespoons orange juice

1 teaspoon grated lemon zest

1 tablespoon lemon juice

1 tablespoon olive oil

1 teaspoon honey

³/₄ teaspoon ground coriander

¹/₄ teaspoon salt

¹/₈ teaspoon black pepper

▲ 3 cups coarsely shredded carrots

2 large shallots, chopped

8 pimiento-stuffed green olives, coarsely chopped

▲ 4 cups mixed salad greens

**PER SERVING** (1 cup greens with ³/₄ cup carrot salad):
111 Cal, 5 g Total Fat, 1 g Sat Fat,
0 g Trans Fat, 0 mg Chol,
384 mg Sod, 16 g Carb, 7 g Sugar,
4 g Fib, 2 g Prot, 35 mg Calc.

**1** Whisk together orange juice, lemon zest and juice, oil, honey, coriander, salt, and pepper in large bowl. Stir in carrots, shallots, and olives. Cover and refrigerate 30 minutes.

**2** Divide salad greens evenly among 4 serving plates. Top evenly with carrot salad and serve at once.

**FYI** To add more protein and fiber, you can add a 15 ¹/₂-ounce can chickpeas, rinsed and drained, to the salad. The per-serving *PointsPlus* value will increase by *1*.

▲ **1 pound sugar snap peas, trimmed**

▲ **3 cups loosely packed arugula or pea shoots**

▲ **1 cup radishes, thinly sliced**

**2 teaspoons grated lemon zest**

**1 tablespoon lemon juice**

**2 teaspoons olive oil**

**¹/₂ teaspoon ground cumin**

**¹/₄ teaspoon salt**

**¹/₄ cup reduced-fat feta cheese, crumbled**

**PER SERVING (1¹/₂ cups):**
96 Cal, 4 g Total Fat, 1 g Sat Fat,
0 g Trans Fat, 3 mg Chol,
283 mg Sod, 11 g Carb, 5 g Sugar,
4 g Fib, 6 g Prot, 107 mg Calc.

# Lemony Pea and Arugula Salad

**1** Combine peas, arugula, and radishes in large bowl.

**2** To make dressing, whisk together lemon zest and juice, oil, cumin, and salt in small bowl. Drizzle dressing over vegetables and toss to coat. Divide salad evenly among 4 plates and sprinkle with feta.

**FYI** Sugar snap peas can be eaten raw—they have a crisp texture and sweet flavor. If you would like to cook them first to soften them slightly, simmer the peas in a saucepan of boiling water for 1 minute, then drain in a colander. Rinse them under cold running water until cool.

LEMONY PEA AND
ARUGULA SALAD

▲ 1 pound green beans, trimmed

▲ 3 navel oranges

1 tablespoon olive oil

1 teaspoon balsamic vinegar

1 teaspoon reduced-sodium
soy sauce

¹⁄₈ teaspoon ground ginger

¹⁄₈ teaspoon salt

▲ 2 scallions, cut diagonally
into thin slices

1 tablespoon sesame seeds

**PER SERVING (1 cup):**
134 Cal, 5 g Total Fat, 1 g Sat Fat,
0 g Trans Fat, 0 mg Chol,
131 mg Sod, 23 g Carb, 11 g Sugar,
7 g Fib, 4 g Prot, 100 mg Calc.

# Green Bean and Orange Salad

**1** Place green beans in steamer basket and set in large skillet over 1 inch of boiling water. Cover tightly and steam until crisp-tender, about 5 minutes. Rinse beans under cold water until cool.

**2** Meanwhile, grate ¹⁄₂ teaspoon zest from 1 orange and place in large bowl. With sharp knife, peel oranges, removing all white pith. Working over same bowl, cut between membranes to release segments. Add oil, vinegar, soy sauce, ginger, and salt to orange segment mixture.

**3** Add beans, scallions, and sesame seeds and toss to combine. Serve at room temperature.

**FYI** If you have one on hand, you can add a thinly sliced yellow or green bell pepper to the steamer basket with the green beans during the last 2 minutes of cooking.

2 tablespoons blue cheese, crumbled

2 tablespoons red-wine vinegar

1 tablespoon extra-virgin olive oil

¼ teaspoon salt

¼ teaspoon black pepper

▲ 4 cups baby spinach

▲ 1 cup thinly sliced
white mushrooms

▲ 1 cup cherry tomatoes, halved

▲ ½ red onion, thinly sliced

PER SERVING (1½ cups):
81 Cal, 5 g Total Fat, 1 g Sat Fat,
0 g Trans Fat, 3 mg Chol,
250 mg Sod, 7 g Carb, 3 g Sugar,
2 g Fib, 3 g Prot, 50 mg Calc

# Spinach and Mushroom Salad with Blue Cheese Dressing

**1**  To make dressing, whisk together cheese, vinegar, oil, salt, and pepper in large serving bowl.

**2**  Add spinach, mushrooms, tomatoes, and onion; toss to coat evenly. Serve at once.

**FYI**  To turn this into a main dish, top each salad with 3 ounces of grilled skinless boneless chicken breast. The per-serving ***PointsPlus*** value will increase by **3**.

**Vegetables** Salads

# Vegetable Salad with Tahini Dressing

SERVES 4

UNDER 20 MINUTES

3 tablespoons tahini

3 tablespoons lemon juice

2 tablespoons warm water

1 small garlic clove, minced

1/2 teaspoon ground cumin

1/2 teaspoon salt

1/8 teaspoon red pepper flakes

▲ 8 radishes, thinly sliced

▲ 4 scallions, thinly sliced

▲ 2 cups cherry tomatoes, halved

▲ 1 English (seedless) cucumber, halved lengthwise and sliced

**PER SERVING (1¼ cups):**
99 Cal, 6 g Total Fat, 1 g Sat Fat, 0 g Trans Fat, 0 mg Chol, 305 mg Sod, 10 g Carb, 4 g Sugar, 3 g Fib, 4 g Prot, 56 mg Calc.

To make dressing, whisk together tahini, lemon juice, water, garlic, cumin, salt, and pepper flakes in large bowl. Add radishes, scallions, tomatoes, and cucumber; toss to coat. Serve at once or cover and refrigerate up to 2 hours and serve chilled.

**FYI** Tahini, a creamy ground sesame paste, is what gives Middle Eastern dishes such as hummus and baba ghanoush their enticing sesame flavor. Look for it in the ethnic section of most large supermarkets. In this recipe, it's used to make a lemony dressing for a salad of crunchy vegetables.

# Zucchini, Basil, and Tomato Salad

**SERVES 4**

**UNDER 20 MINUTES**

▲ 2 cups lightly packed mixed baby greens

▲ 2 plum tomatoes, each cut into eighths

▲ 1 medium zucchini, thinly sliced

¼ cup packed fresh basil leaves

1 tablespoon white-wine vinegar

1 tablespoon olive oil

¼ teaspoon salt

¼ teaspoon black pepper

**PER SERVING** (about 1 cup):
49 Cal, 4 g Total Fat, 1 g Sat Fat,
0 g Trans Fat, 0 mg Chol,
162 mg Sod, 4 g Carb, 2 g Sugar,
2 g Fib, 1 g Prot, 16 mg Calc.

**1** Place greens, tomatoes, zucchini, and basil in large serving bowl.

**2** To make dressing, whisk together remaining ingredients in small bowl. Drizzle dressing over greens mixture and toss to coat. Serve at once.

**FYI** To thinly slice the zucchini, use a mandoline, the slicing attachment of a food processor, or the slicing blade of a box grater.

GRILLED CORN, PEPPER, AND
TOMATO SALAD WITH LIME

# Grilled Corn, Pepper, and Tomato Salad with Lime

SERVES 6

▲ 4 ears corn on the cob

▲ 4 large Italian frying peppers
or poblano peppers, halved
lengthwise and seeded

3 teaspoons olive oil

▲ 4 large plum tomatoes, halved
lengthwise

½ teaspoon chili powder

½ cup chopped fresh cilantro

▲ ¼ cup chopped sweet onion

3 tablespoons fresh lime juice

1 teaspoon ground cumin

½ teaspoon salt

¼ teaspoon black pepper

PER SERVING ( ¾ cup):
119 Cal, 4 g Total Fat, 1 g Sat Fat,
0 g Trans Fat, 0 mg Chol,
213 mg Sod, 20 g Carb, 3 g Sugar,
5 g Fib, 4 g Prot, 19 mg Calc.

**1** Spray grill rack with nonstick spray. Preheat grill to medium or prepare medium fire.

**2** Pull back husks of corn; remove silks. Rinse corn with water. Pull corn husks back over kernels, twisting ends to secure husks. Combine peppers and 1 teaspoon oil in medium bowl; toss to coat. Sprinkle cut sides of tomatoes with chili powder.

**3** Place corn, peppers, and tomatoes on grill rack, arranging tomatoes cut side up. Grill, turning corn every 2 minutes, until grill marks appear all over husks, 15–17 minutes. Grill peppers, turning once, until tender and lightly charred, 6–8 minutes. Grill tomatoes, without turning, until skins begin to char, about 5 minutes.

**4** When cool enough to handle, peel husks from corn and cut kernels from corn. Place kernels in large bowl. Slice peppers; add to corn. Chop tomatoes; add to corn mixture. Add cilantro, onion, lime juice, cumin, salt, black pepper, and remaining 2 teaspoons oil and toss to combine. Serve at room temperature.

**FYI** When you grill the vegetables for this recipe, throw a few extra peppers on the grill at the same time. You can use them in sandwiches, pasta dishes, or a salsa later in the week.

# Roasted Vegetable and White Bean Salad

SERVES 4

▲ 1 medium fennel bulb, sliced (fronds reserved)

▲ 1 small red onion, halved and sliced

▲ ½ pound green beans, trimmed and cut in half

▲ ½ pound cremini mushrooms, quartered

4 teaspoons olive oil

2 large garlic cloves, minced

½ teaspoon salt

¼ teaspoon dried oregano

¼ teaspoon red pepper flakes

▲ 1 tablespoon reduced-sodium vegetable broth

1 tablespoon lemon juice

▲ 1 pound plum or other small tomatoes, cut into ½-inch pieces

▲ 1 (15½-ounce) can cannellini (white kidney) beans, rinsed and drained

**PER SERVING (1½ cups):**
215 Cal, 5 g Total Fat, 1 g Sat Fat,
0 g Trans Fat, 0 mg Chol,
624 mg Sod, 35 g Carb, 7 g Sugar,
11 g Fib, 11 g Prot, 131 mg Calc.

**1** Preheat oven to 425°F. Coat large rimmed baking pan with nonstick spray.

**2** Place fennel, onion, green beans, and mushrooms in pan. Drizzle with 2 teaspoons oil, sprinkle with garlic, salt, oregano, and pepper flakes and toss to coat. Arrange vegetables in single layer and roast, stirring occasionally, until vegetables are tender and lightly browned, about 30 minutes.

**3** Meanwhile, whisk together broth, lemon juice, and remaining 2 teaspoons oil in large bowl. Stir in tomatoes, cannellini beans, and roasted vegetables. Chop enough of reserved fennel fronds to equal 1 tablespoon and stir into salad. Serve warm or at room temperature.

**FYI** Fresh fennel has a delicate licorice flavor that you either love or hate. If it's not your favorite, substitute a red or yellow bell pepper for the fennel bulb in this recipe, and instead of the chopped fennel fronds, use chopped fresh parsley or basil.

ROASTED VEGETABLE
AND WHITE BEAN SALAD

# Creamy Potato and Apple Salad

SERVES 6

▲ 1 pound red potatoes, scrubbed and cut into 1-inch chunks

2 teaspoons apple-cider vinegar

▲ ¼ cup plain fat-free yogurt

3 tablespoons reduced-fat mayonnaise

1 teaspoon whole-grain mustard

½ teaspoon salt

⅛ teaspoon black pepper

▲ 2 medium celery stalks with leaves, sliced

▲ 1 large Granny Smith apple, quartered, cored, and thinly sliced

▲ ¾ cup halved red seedless grapes

▲ 2 scallions, thinly sliced

2 tablespoons walnuts, toasted and coarsely chopped

**PER SERVING (1 cup):**
127 Cal, 3 g Total Fat, 0 g Sat Fat,
0 g Trans Fat, 0 mg Chol,
302 mg Sod, 25 g Carb, 10 g Sugar,
3 g Fib, 3 g Prot, 46 mg Calc.

**1** Place potatoes in medium saucepan with enough water to cover by 1 inch; bring to boil and cook until fork-tender, about 10 minutes. Drain and transfer to medium bowl; drizzle with vinegar and toss to coat. Let stand until cool.

**2** To make dressing, whisk together yogurt, mayonnaise, mustard, salt, and pepper in large bowl. Add potatoes, celery, apple, grapes, and scallions; toss to coat. Sprinkle with walnuts just before serving. Serve at once or cover and refrigerate up to 2 hours and serve chilled.

**FYI** You can add some protein and make this salad more filling by adding 3 chopped hard-cooked eggs (the per-serving *PointsPlus* value will increase by *1*).

# Thai-Style Cabbage Salad

¹/₃ cup water

3 tablespoons rice vinegar

1 teaspoon sugar

¹/₄ teaspoon salt

¹/₄ teaspoon red pepper flakes

▲ 4 cups thinly sliced Napa cabbage

▲ 4 scallions, cut diagonally
into thin slices

▲ 1 English (seedless) cucumber,
halved lengthwise and sliced

¹/₄ cup chopped fresh cilantro

2 tablespoons thinly sliced fresh
Thai basil or fresh mint leaves

1 tablespoon lime juice

2 tablespoons chopped unsalted
dry-roasted peanuts

**PER SERVING (1¹/₄ cups):**
55 Cal, 2 g Total Fat, 0 g Sat Fat,
0 g Trans Fat, 0 mg Chol,
178 mg Sod, 7 g Carb, 3 g Sugar,
3 g Fib, 3 g Prot, 71 mg Calc.

**1**  To make dressing, stir together water, vinegar, sugar, salt, and pepper flakes in small saucepan and bring to boil over high heat, stirring to dissolve sugar. Reduce heat and simmer, uncovered, stirring occasionally, until mixture is reduced slightly, 5 minutes.

**2**  Combine cabbage, scallions, and cucumber in large bowl. Add vinegar mixture, cilantro, basil, and lime juice and toss to coat. Cover and refrigerate up to 2 hours before serving. Sprinkle with peanuts just before serving.

**FYI**  If Napa cabbage isn't available, you can make this crunchy slaw with green or red cabbage (or a combination of both for a colorful presentation) or with crinkly-leaved Savoy cabbage.

**Vegetables** Salads

ASIAN PEANUT SLAW

# Asian Peanut Slaw

SERVES 4

UNDER 20 MINUTES

3 tablespoons rice vinegar

2 tablespoons reduced-sodium soy sauce

2 tablespoons creamy peanut butter

1 tablespoon chopped peeled fresh ginger

1 small garlic clove, chopped

1 tablespoon honey

▲ ½ head Savoy cabbage, thinly sliced (about 5 cups)

▲ 1 yellow bell pepper, cut into thin strips

▲ 1 large carrot, cut into thin strips

▲ 2 scallions, thinly sliced

¼ cup chopped fresh cilantro

2 tablespoons unsalted dry-roasted peanuts, chopped

**1**  To make dressing, combine vinegar, soy sauce, peanut butter, ginger, garlic, and honey in blender and process until smooth.

**2**  Combine cabbage, bell pepper, carrot, scallions, and cilantro in large bowl. Add dressing and toss to coat. Sprinkle with peanuts just before serving.

**FYI**  This slightly sweet peanut dressing is delicious to toss with a pasta salad or to serve as a dip with fresh veggies.

**PER SERVING (1¼ cups):**
142 Cal, 6 g Total Fat, 1 g Sat Fat,
0 g Trans Fat, 0 mg Chol,
344 mg Sod, 19 g Carb, 10 g Sugar,
5 g Fib, 6 g Prot, 56 mg Calc.

# Roasted Beets with Horseradish-Mustard Dressing

SERVES 4

▲ 3 medium beets (1 pound), trimmed and scrubbed

¼ cup water

1 tablespoon plus 1 teaspoon prepared horseradish, drained

1 tablespoon olive oil

2 teaspoons maple syrup

1½ teaspoons balsamic vinegar

1 teaspoon whole-grain mustard

⅛ teaspoon salt

1 tablespoon minced fresh chives

PER SERVING (½ cup):
94 Cal, 4 g Total Fat, 1 g Sat Fat, 0 g Trans Fat, 0 mg Chol, 217 mg Sod, 14 g Carb, 10 g Sugar, 3 g Fib, 2 g Prot, 29 mg Calc.

**1** Preheat oven to 400°F.

**2** Place beets in medium baking dish; add water to dish. Cover and bake until beets are fork-tender, 1 hour 15 minutes. Let stand until cool enough to handle, 20 minutes. Peel beets and thinly slice.

**3** Meanwhile, whisk together horseradish, oil, maple syrup, vinegar, mustard, and salt in large bowl. Add beets and chives; toss to coat. Serve warm or at room temperature.

**FYI** If you buy beets with the leaves still attached for this recipe, rinse and coarsely chop them, then steam until tender. Toss them with the dressing along with the beet roots.

# Gingery Stir-Fried Cabbage

SERVES 4

UNDER 20 MINUTES

2 teaspoons canola oil

1 tablespoon minced peeled fresh ginger

2 garlic cloves, minced

▲ 6 cups thinly sliced green cabbage

▲ 2 carrots, shredded

▲ 2 scallions, thinly sliced

2 tablespoons reduced-sodium soy sauce

1 tablespoon seasoned rice vinegar

1 teaspoon chili-garlic paste

1/2 teaspoon Asian (dark) sesame oil

**PER SERVING** (about 3/4 cup): 73 Cal, 3 g Total Fat, 0 g Sat Fat, 0 g Trans Fat, 0 mg Chol, 337 mg Sod, 11 g Carb, 2 g Sugar, 4 g Fib, 2 g Prot, 69 mg Calc.

**1** Heat large heavy skillet or wok over medium heat until drop of water sizzles in pan; add canola oil and swirl to coat pan. Add ginger and garlic and cook, stirring constantly, until fragrant, about 1 minute.

**2** Add cabbage and carrots and cook, stirring occasionally, until softened, about 8 minutes. Remove skillet from heat and stir in scallions, soy sauce, vinegar, chili-garlic paste, and sesame oil. Serve at once.

**FYI** Instead of the green cabbage, you can make this dish with Savoy, Napa, or red cabbage.

# Brussels Sprouts with Chickpeas and Grapes

SERVES 4

▲ 1 pound Brussels sprouts, trimmed and halved

2 teaspoons olive oil

1 large shallot, minced

2 garlic cloves, minced

1 tablespoon chopped fresh thyme

▲ 1½ cups halved seedless red grapes

▲ ½ cup canned chickpeas, rinsed and drained

1 tablespoon dry sherry or white grape juice

¼ teaspoon salt

1 teaspoon grated lemon zest

**PER SERVING (1 cup):**
136 Cal, 2 g Total Fat, 0 g Sat Fat, 0 g Trans Fat, 0 mg Chol, 291 mg Sod, 27 g Carb, 12 g Sugar, 6 g Fib, 6 g Prot, 67 mg Calc.

**1** Place Brussels sprouts in steamer basket and set in large skillet over 1 inch of boiling water. Cover tightly and steam until tender, about 10 minutes.

**2** Heat oil in large nonstick skillet over medium heat. Add shallot, garlic, and thyme and cook, stirring constantly, until shallot is softened, about 2 minutes. Add grapes and cook, stirring frequently, until softened, about 3 minutes.

**3** Add Brussels sprouts, chickpeas, sherry, and salt. Cook, stirring frequently, until chickpeas are heated through, 3–4 minutes. Sprinkle with lemon zest.

**BRUSSELS SPROUTS WITH
CHICKPEAS AND GRAPES**

▲ ½ large head cauliflower, trimmed and cut into small florets (about 5 cups)

1 tablespoon olive oil

½ cup whole wheat panko (bread crumbs)

2 tablespoons grated Parmesan cheese

2 teaspoons grated lemon zest

¼ teaspoon dried thyme

¼ teaspoon salt

⅛ teaspoon black pepper

2 tablespoons lemon juice

3 tablespoons minced fresh chives

**PER SERVING (1 cup):**
120 Cal, 5 g Total Fat, 1 g Sat Fat, 0 g Trans Fat, 2 mg Chol, 232 mg Sod, 17 g Carb, 3 g Sugar, 4 g Fib, 5 g Prot, 56 mg Calc.

# Cauliflower with Lemon-Chive Crumbs

**1**  Place cauliflower in steamer basket and set in large skillet over 1 inch boiling water. Cover tightly and steam until tender, about 8 minutes.

**2**  Heat oil in large nonstick skillet over medium heat. Add crumbs, cheese, lemon zest, thyme, salt, and pepper; cook, stirring constantly, until crumbs are toasted, about 3 minutes.

**3**  Remove from heat. Add cauliflower, lemon juice, and chives and toss to mix well.

**FYI**  This dish is also delicious made with broccoli instead of cauliflower. If you use broccoli, reduce the steaming time to about 5 minutes.

# Lemon-Thyme Mashed Potatoes

**SERVES 4**

▲ 1¼ pounds baby red potatoes, scrubbed and halved

▲ ½ cup fat-free milk

2 teaspoons unsalted butter

½ teaspoon salt

¼ teaspoon black pepper

1 tablespoon grated lemon zest

2 teaspoons lemon juice

2 teaspoons chopped fresh thyme

**PER SERVING (³/₄ cup):**
129 Cal, 2 g Total Fat, 1 g Sat Fat,
0 g Trans Fat, 6 mg Chol,
313 mg Sod, 25 g Carb, 3 g Sugar,
3 g Fib, 4 g Prot, 58 mg Calc.

**1** Place potatoes in medium saucepan with enough water to cover by 1 inch; bring to boil over high heat. Reduce heat and simmer until potatoes are tender, about 20 minutes; drain.

**2** Return potatoes to saucepan. Add milk, butter, salt, and pepper. Mash until potatoes are smooth. Stir in lemon zest and juice and thyme.

**FYI** Keeping the skins on the potatoes adds texture, fiber, and nutrients as well as saving on prep time.

**SPICE-ROASTED FINGERLING POTATOES WITH SNAP PEAS**

# Spice-Roasted Fingerling Potatoes with Snap Peas

SERVES 4

1 teaspoon ground cumin

³/₄ teaspoon ground coriander

¹/₂ teaspoon salt

¹/₄ teaspoon ground turmeric

¹/₄ teaspoon cayenne

▲ 1 pound fingerling potatoes, scrubbed and halved lengthwise

2 teaspoons olive oil

2 garlic cloves, minced

▲ ³/₄ cup plain fat-free yogurt

▲ ¹/₄ cup chopped peeled cucumber

1 tablespoon chopped fresh parsley or mint

▲ 1 (8-ounce) package microwave-ready sugar snap peas

**PER SERVING (1 cup vegetables with ¹/₄ cup sauce):** 160 Cal, 3 g Total Fat, 0 g Sat Fat, 0 g Trans Fat, 1 mg Chol, 335 mg Sod, 29 g Carb, 7 g Sugar, 4 g Fib, 7 g Prot, 141 mg Calc.

**1** Preheat oven to 375°F. Spray 9 x 13-inch baking dish with nonstick spray.

**2** Stir together cumin, coriander, salt, turmeric, and cayenne in small cup. Transfer ¹/₂ teaspoon spice mix to medium bowl for making sauce.

**3** Place potatoes in baking dish. Add oil, garlic, and remaining spice mixture and toss to coat. Roast, turning potatoes occasionally, until browned and tender, 35–40 minutes.

**4** Meanwhile, to make sauce, add yogurt, cucumber, and parsley to reserved spice mixture and stir to mix well. Cover and refrigerate until ready to serve.

**5** When potatoes are almost done, microwave peas according to package directions. Combine potatoes and peas in large bowl and toss to combine. Serve vegetables with sauce.

**FYI** If fingerling potatoes aren't available, use small Yukon Gold potatoes and cut them into quarters before roasting.

# Grilled Green Tomatoes with Creole Mayonnaise

SERVES 4

UNDER 20 MINUTES

2 tablespoons reduced-fat
mayonnaise

▲ 2 tablespoons fat-free sour cream

2 teaspoons lemon juice

³/₄ teaspoon Creole seasoning

▲ 4 medium green tomatoes, cored
and cut into ¹/₂-inch slices

2 teaspoons canola oil

¹/₈ teaspoon salt

¹/₈ teaspoon black pepper

**PER SERVING (3 tomato slices with
1 tablespoon mayonnaise):**
69 Cal, 4 g Total Fat, 0 g Sat Fat,
0 g Trans Fat, 1 mg Chol,
278 mg Sod, 9 g Carb, 6 g Sugar,
1 g Fib, 2 g Prot, 27 mg Calc.

**1** Stir together mayonnaise, sour cream, lemon juice, and Creole seasoning in small bowl. Cover and refrigerate until ready to serve.

**2** Spray grill rack with nonstick spray. Preheat grill to medium or prepare medium fire.

**3** Place tomatoes in large bowl. Drizzle with oil, sprinkle with salt and pepper, and toss to coat. Place tomatoes on grill rack; grill until tomatoes are lightly charred, about 5 minutes on each side. Serve tomatoes with mayonnaise.

**FYI** If you can't find green tomatoes, you can make this recipe with firm, slightly under-ripe regular tomatoes. You may need to reduce the grilling time by a minute or two on each side.

# Roasted Root Vegetables with Cumin Seeds

**SERVES 6**

▲ 8 large radishes, halved

▲ 4 small turnips, peeled, halved, and sliced

▲ 3 large carrots, cut into ³/₄-inch pieces

▲ 2 medium parsnips, peeled and cut into ³/₄-inch pieces

▲ 1 large onion, halved and sliced

8 garlic cloves, peeled

▲ 2 tablespoons reduced-sodium vegetable broth

1 tablespoon olive oil

1 ¹/₂ teaspoons cumin seeds

¹/₂ teaspoon salt

¹/₄ teaspoon black pepper

**PER SERVING (1 cup):**
105 Cal, 3 g Total Fat, 0 g Sat Fat, 0 g Trans Fat, 0 mg Chol, 261 mg Sod, 20 g Carb, 7 g Sugar, 4 g Fib, 2 g Prot, 66 mg Calc.

**3** PointsPlus® value

**1** Preheat oven to 400°F. Spray 9 x 13-inch baking dish with nonstick spray.

**2** Combine radishes, turnips, carrots, parsnips, onion, and garlic in dish. Add broth, oil, cumin seeds, salt, and pepper and toss to coat. Roast, stirring occasionally, until vegetables are browned and tender, about 1 hour.

**FYI** You can turn this dish into a salad. To do so, just before serving, toss together 4 cups baby arugula or baby spinach and 2 tablespoons lemon juice in a large bowl. Add the roasted vegetables and toss to combine.

# Asian Baked Kabocha Squash

SERVES 6

▲ 1 kabocha squash, about 2 1/2 pounds
1/4 teaspoon salt
1 tablespoon olive oil
1 teaspoon honey
1/4 teaspoon five-spice powder
1 tablespoon toasted sesame seeds
1 tablespoon chopped fresh cilantro

**PER SERVING (1 wedge):**
93 Cal, 4 g Total Fat, 0 g Sat Fat, 0 g Trans Fat, 0 mg Chol, 101 mg Sod, 15 g Carb, 6 g Sugar, 5 g Fib, 2 g Prot, 41 mg Calc.

**1** Preheat oven to 375°F. Spray 9 x 13-inch baking dish with nonstick spray.

**2** Cut squash in half lengthwise; scoop out seeds. Cut each half into 3 wedges. Arrange wedges, skin side down, in dish; sprinkle with salt. Stir together oil, honey, and five-spice powder in small bowl; drizzle over squash.

**3** Bake until squash is tender, about 1 hour. Sprinkle with sesame seeds and cilantro.

**FYI** Kabocha is a round, squat, thick-fleshed Japanese variety of winter squash. Depending on the variety, the skin of kabocha can be green, gray, or orange. Whatever the color, the flesh is smooth, bright orange, and sweet.

ASIAN BAKED
KABOCHA SQUASH

**PARMESAN-HERB BROILED TOMATOES**

# Parmesan-Herb Broiled Tomatoes

SERVES 4

UNDER 20 MINUTES

▲ 8 plum tomatoes, halved lengthwise

1 tablespoon chopped fresh thyme

2 teaspoons extra-virgin olive oil

½ teaspoon salt

½ teaspoon black pepper

2 tablespoons grated Parmesan cheese

2 tablespoons chopped fresh basil

**PER SERVING (4 tomato halves):**
55 Cal, 3 g Total Fat, 1 g Sat Fat,
0 g Trans Fat, 2 mg Chol,
335 mg Sod, 5 g Carb, 3 g Sugar,
2 g Fib, 2 g Prot, 45 mg Calc.

1 PointsPlus® value

**1** Preheat broiler and spray broiler rack with nonstick spray.

**2** Toss together tomatoes, thyme, oil, salt, and pepper in large bowl. Arrange tomatoes, cut side up, on broiler rack. Broil 6 inches from heat until tomatoes are tender and lightly charred, about 5 minutes on each side.

**3** Transfer tomatoes to platter; sprinkle with Parmesan cheese and basil. Serve hot, warm, or at room temperature.

**FYI** If you don't have fresh herbs on hand, toss the tomatoes with 1 teaspoon dried thyme before broiling and omit the fresh basil. The flavor won't be quite the same, but the tomatoes will still be delicious.

# Fruits

Soups, Salads, and Desserts

# Fruits

5 servings of fruits and vegetables per day; 9 servings if you weigh more than 350 pounds. A serving of fruit is ½ cup.

## WHY THEY'RE ESSENTIAL

**Fruits are a big zero!** With the *PointsPlus* plan, all fruits have **0 *PointsPlus*** value, which means you don't have to count them. This makes them perfect to enjoy when you're having an afternoon slump and crave a treat or when you want a *PointsPlus*-free dessert with lunch or dinner.

**Fruits are truly powerful.** They are packed with fiber, antioxidants, vitamins, and minerals. Eating fruit with a meal or as a snack helps you feel satisfied and can help you lose weight even if you're eating higher calorie fruits such as bananas. One word of caution: As with any food, eat fruit until you're satisfied, not until you're stuffed.

**Citrus is not the only source of C.** Everyone knows citrus is an excellent source of vitamin C, but most other fruits contain a good amount of this vital nutrient too. Vitamin C is required for growth and repair of tissues, helps with wound healing, and important for dental health.

## WHAT TO BUY

**Fresh fruits:** Make selections based on what's in season for freshness and flavor.

*TIP: Get fresh fruit at a great price, and some exercise too, by seeking out a local pick-your-own farm in the summer.*

**Frozen fruits:** Select only unsweetened frozen fruits.

*TIP: Freeze your own berries in the summer to make delicious winter desserts and smoothies.*

**Canned fruits:** Buy fruits canned in water without added sugar or fruit juices.

*TIP: Though they are more expensive, purchasing single-serve unsweetened applesauce cups makes it easy to have a healthy snack.*

## GOOD TO KNOW

**Choose whole fruits over fruit juice.** Whole fruit contains fiber, which slows digestion and makes you feel fuller. And juices are not Power Foods; you have to count their *PointsPlus* values.

**Fruits are full of phytochemicals.** Phytochemicals are naturally occurring compounds that have antioxidant properties that laboratory studies show may do everything from strengthening the immune system to preventing cancer. Researchers are just learning about their importance, but consuming a wide variety of fruits (as well as vegetables) is an excellent idea to ensure the best possible health.

**Berries** such as blackberries, blueberries, strawberries, and raspberries

**POWER-UP IDEAS**

- Berries are easy to add to cereal, granola, or oatmeal at breakfast.
- Make a Power Food smoothie with frozen berries and plain fat-free yogurt.
- Puree fresh berries with a little water, then freeze in small paper drink cups for a healthy ice pop treat.

**TAKE NOTE**

- Replacing high-calorie snacks like cookies and chips with fruit can help you consume fewer calories and more nutrients.
- Most fruits are a good source of potassium, which helps maintain healthy blood pressure.
- Blueberries are one of the most antioxidant-rich foods and they're an excellent source of fiber and vitamins A and C.

**Tree fruits** such as apples, apricots, bananas, cherries, nectarines, peaches, and pears

**POWER-UP IDEAS**

- Keep fruit in sight. A bowl of apples and pears on your desk or counter will remind you to eat them.
- These fruits are the ultimate in portable snacking—keep them in your purse, at your desk, and in the car.
- Fruits are not just for sweet dishes. Make a mango salsa for fish or add sliced apples to a green salad.

**TAKE NOTE**

- Fruits are low in sodium and fat and they have no cholesterol.
- Eat apples with the peel; it provides a large part of fiber and antioxidants.
- Consuming cherries may help relieve the pain of arthritis and gout.
- One kiwifruit has all the vitamin C you need in a day.
- Fruits do contain natural sugars, but because they also have fiber and a wide array of other nutrients, they are a healthier choice than a sugary dessert.

**Citrus fruits and melons**

**POWER-UP IDEAS**

- Separate oranges into segments and carry in a resealable plastic bag for easy eating during your commute.
- Section pink grapefruit and serve with thinly sliced avocado for a colorful and delicious salad.
- Melons, with their refreshing taste and high water content, are a great after-workout treat.

**TAKE NOTE**

- Red and pink grapefruit are an excellent source of vitamin A.
- Oranges are a good source of folate and fiber and they also contain antioxidants.
- Watermelon and cantaloupe are good sources of vitamin C, vitamin A, and potassium.
- Honeydew is the sweetest of the melons, making it the perfect summer dessert.

## In this chapter

# Pear-Scented Butternut Squash Soup

SERVES 6

▲ 1 (1 ½-pound) butternut squash, peeled, seeded, and cut into ¾-inch pieces

▲ 1 pear, peeled, cored, and sliced

▲ 1 sweet onion, chopped

▲ 1 (14-ounce) can reduced-sodium chicken broth

2 teaspoons tomato paste

¼ teaspoon dried sage

¼ teaspoon dried thyme

¼ teaspoon salt

⅛ teaspoon black pepper

▲ 6 tablespoons fat-free sour cream

PER SERVING (¾ cup soup with 1 tablespoon sour cream): 89 Cal, 1 g Total Fat, 0 g Sat Fat, 0 g Trans Fat, 1 mg Chol, 159 mg Sod, 20 g Carb, 7 g Sugar, 4 g Fib, 3 g Prot, 74 mg Calc.

**1** Preheat oven to 400°F. Spray large rimmed baking sheet with nonstick spray.

**2** Place squash, pear, and onion on pan; spray lightly with nonstick spray. Toss to coat. Roast, stirring occasionally, until vegetables are tender, 45 minutes.

**3** Place vegetable mixture in blender in batches, adding half of broth to each batch, and puree. Transfer to medium saucepan. Add tomato paste, sage, thyme, salt, and pepper. Bring to simmer over medium heat, stirring occasionally. Ladle soup evenly into 6 bowls and top evenly with sour cream.

**FYI** This delicious autumnal soup freezes and reheats beautifully. Make a double batch and freeze up to 3 months.

# Cold Grape and Cucumber Soup

SERVES 4

1 slice whole wheat sandwich bread

▲ 1¼ cups green seedless grapes

¼ cup cilantro leaves

1 small garlic clove, chopped

▲ 1 large cucumber, peeled, seeded, and chopped

▲ 1 medium green bell pepper, chopped

▲ 2 scallions, chopped

▲ 1 jalapeño pepper, seeded and chopped

¾ cup canned tomatillos, rinsed and drained

2 tablespoons fresh lime juice

1 teaspoon extra-virgin olive oil

½ teaspoon ground cumin

▲ 4 tablespoons plain fat-free Greek yogurt

**PER SERVING** (¾ cup soup with 1 tablespoon yogurt):
106 Cal, 2 g Total Fat, 0 g Sat Fat,
0 g Trans Fat, 0 mg Chol,
44 mg Sod, 19 g Carb, 11 g Sugar,
3 g Fib, 4 g Prot, 45 mg Calc.

1  Place bread in shallow dish; add cold water to cover. Let stand 5 minutes to soften. Drain and squeeze water from bread.

2  Combine bread, grapes, cilantro, and garlic in blender and process until smooth, about 1 minute. Add cucumber, bell pepper, scallions, jalapeño, tomatillos, lime juice, oil and cumin; process until smooth.

3  Cover and refrigerate until well chilled, at least 3 hours or up to 8 hours. Ladle soup evenly into 4 bowls and top evenly with yogurt.

**FYI**  In addition to the yogurt, you can top each serving of the soup with ¼ cup chopped grapes or fresh tomatoes.

# Chilled Raspberry and Beet Soup

SERVES 6

▲ 3 medium beets, peeled and chopped (1 pound)

▲ ¹/₂ medium Yukon Gold potato, peeled and chopped

▲ ¹/₂ medium onion, chopped

▲ 1 (14-ounce) can reduced-sodium chicken broth

1 cup water

¹/₂ teaspoon dried tarragon

¹/₄ teaspoon dried thyme

¹/₂ teaspoon salt

▲ 1¹/₂ cups fresh or thawed frozen raspberries

1¹/₂ tablespoons white-wine vinegar

2 teaspoons honey

6 tablespoons light sour cream

Fresh tarragon and thyme sprigs, for garnish (optional)

PER SERVING (³/₄ cup soup with 1 tablespoon sour cream): 95 Cal, 3 g Total Fat, 1 g Sat Fat, 0 g Trans Fat, 5 mg Chol, 260 mg Sod, 15 g Carb, 7 g Sugar, 4 g Fib, 4 g Prot, 46 mg Calc.

1  Combine beets, potato, onion, broth, water, tarragon, thyme, and salt in large saucepan; bring to boil. Reduce heat and simmer, covered, until beets are very tender, 45 minutes. Let cool about 10 minutes.

2  Pour soup, in batches, into blender and puree, adding raspberries to one batch. Press puree through a strainer; discard seeds. Stir in vinegar and honey.

3  Cover and refrigerate until well chilled, at least 3 hours or up to 8 hours. Ladle soup evenly into 6 bowls and top evenly with sour cream. Sprinkle with tarragon and thyme, if using.

**CHILLED RASPBERRY AND BEET SOUP**

# Herbed Watermelon and Tomato Salad

SERVES 4

UNDER 20 MINUTES

2 tablespoons red-wine vinegar

2 teaspoons olive oil

¼ teaspoon salt

⅛ teaspoon cayenne

▲ 3 cups diced seedless watermelon

▲ 3 cups diced fresh tomatoes

⅓ cup torn fresh basil leaves

2 tablespoons chopped fresh mint

1 tablespoon minced fresh chives

**PER SERVING (1⅓ cups):**
82 Cal, 3 g Total Fat, 0 g Sat Fat,
0 g Trans Fat, 0 mg Chol,
154 mg Sod, 14 g Carb, 11 g Sugar,
2 g Fib, 2 g Prot, 31 mg Calc

1   To make dressing, whisk together vinegar, oil, salt, and cayenne in large bowl.

2   Add watermelon, tomatoes, basil, mint, and chives; toss gently to coat. Serve at once.

**FYI**   To make this a heartier dish, you can add a diced cucumber to the salad and serve it over a bed of mixed baby greens or baby spinach. For an additional *1 PointsPlus* value, you can sprinkle each salad with 1 ounce of crumbled fat-free feta cheese.

# Grilled Pineapple and Tomato Salad

SERVES 4

UNDER 20 MINUTES

▲ ½ fresh pineapple, cored and cut into 8 slices

1 teaspoon sugar

¼ teaspoon ancho chile powder

▲ 1 large tomato, cut into 8 slices

2 tablespoons lime juice

1 tablespoon water

2 teaspoons extra-virgin olive oil

¼ teaspoon salt

¼ teaspoon black pepper

2 tablespoons chopped fresh cilantro

▲ 4 cups mixed salad greens

1 avocado, peeled, pitted, and diced

**PER SERVING (1 plate):**
158 Cal, 8 g Total Fat, 1 g Sat Fat,
0 g Trans Fat, 0 mg Chol,
173 mg Sod, 24 g Carb, 15 g Sugar,
6 g Fib, 2 g Prot, 26 mg Calc.

**1**  Pat pineapple slices dry with paper towels; sprinkle with sugar and chile powder.

**2**  Spray large ridged grill pan with nonstick spray and set over medium-high heat.

**3**  Place pineapple in pan, in batches, if necessary, and cook until golden brown, 3–4 minutes on each side. Transfer to plate. Lightly spray tomato slices with nonstick spray. Place in same pan and grill until softened, about 4 minutes (do not turn). Transfer to plate.

**4**  To make dressing, whisk together lime juice, water, oil, salt, and pepper in small bowl. Stir in cilantro.

**5**  Divide greens among 4 plates; top evenly with pineapple and tomato slices. Drizzle evenly with dressing and sprinkle with avocado.

**FYI**  To make this a heartier salad, you can grill tuna steaks at the same time as you grill the pineapple and tomato. If you top each salad with a 3-ounce grilled tuna steak, increase the per-serving *PointsPlus* value by *3*.

1 tablespoon white
balsamic vinegar

2 teaspoons olive oil

1 teaspoon water

½ teaspoon Dijon mustard

⅛ teaspoon salt

⅛ teaspoon black pepper

▲ 6 cups baby arugula

▲ 1 pear, cored and cut into wedges

▲ 6 fresh figs, halved

¼ cup crumbled goat cheese

2 tablespoons sliced
almonds, toasted

**PER SERVING (1 plate):**
138 Cal, 6 g Total Fat, 2 g Sat Fat,
0 g Trans Fat, 3 mg Chol,
124 mg Sod, 21 g Carb, 16 g Sugar,
4 g Fib, 3 g Prot, 92 mg Calc.

# Fresh Fig and Pear Salad

1  To make dressing, whisk together vinegar, oil, water, mustard, salt, and pepper in large bowl. Add arugula and pear and toss gently to coat.

2  Divide salad evenly among 4 plates; top evenly with figs, cheese, and almonds. Serve at once.

**FYI**  If fresh figs aren't in season, you can make this salad using 1 cup of fresh raspberries or strawberries instead.

**FRESH FIG AND PEAR SALAD**

¼ cup plain low-fat Greek yogurt

2 tablespoons light mayonnaise

1½ tablespoons lemon juice

¼ teaspoon salt

▲ 2 cups diced roasted skinless turkey breast

▲ 2 scallions, thinly sliced

▲ 1 apple, cored and diced

▲ 1 celery stalk, chopped

▲ 1 cup fresh blueberries

▲ 3 cups baby spinach

2 tablespoons chopped walnuts

PER SERVING (1 cup turkey salad
with ¾ cup spinach):
269 Cal, 6 g Total Fat, 1 g Sat Fat,
0 g Trans Fat, 98 mg Chol,
317 mg Sod, 17 g Carb, 10 g Sugar,
4 g Fib, 37 g Prot, 55 mg Calc.

# Blueberry-Turkey Salad with Spinach

1  To make dressing, stir together yogurt, mayonnaise, lemon juice, and salt in large bowl. Add turkey, scallions, apple, celery, and blueberries; toss to coat.

2  Divide spinach among 4 plates; top evenly with turkey salad. Sprinkle with walnuts and serve at once.

FYI  Fresh rotisserie-roasted turkey breast is available in many supermarkets. If you can't find it, you can use roasted skinless chicken breast in this recipe.

# Spiced Cranberry and Pear Cakes

SERVES 6

1 cup all-purpose flour

2 tablespoons ground flax seeds

1/2 teaspoon pumpkin pie spice

1/2 teaspoon baking powder

1/2 teaspoon baking soda

1/8 teaspoon salt

1/4 cup dried cranberries, chopped

2 tablespoons chopped crystallized ginger

1/3 cup sugar

1/4 cup canola oil

▲ 1 large egg

▲ 2 pears, peeled and coarsely shredded

1 teaspoon confectioners' sugar

PER SERVING (1 cake):
271 Cal, 11 g Total Fat, 1 g Sat Fat,
0 g Trans Fat, 36 mg Chol,
212 mg Sod, 41 g Carb, 18 g Sugar,
3 g Fib, 4 g Prot, 24 mg Calc.

1   Preheat oven to 350°F. Spray 6 (1-cup) mini Bundt pans with nonstick spray and dust with flour.

2   Whisk together flour, flax seeds, pumpkin pie spice, baking powder, baking soda, and salt in large bowl. Stir in cranberries and ginger. Whisk together sugar, oil, and egg in medium bowl; stir in pears.

3   Add sugar mixture to flour mixture; stir just until blended. Spoon batter evenly into pans.

4   Bake until toothpick inserted into centers of cakes comes out clean, 22–25 minutes. Let cool in pans on rack 1 minute. Remove cakes from pans and let cool completely on rack. Dust with confectioners' sugar.

FYI   **If you don't have mini-Bundt pans, you can use six 8-ounce baking dishes or large muffin tins to bake the cakes. You can grind flax seed in a clean coffee grinder or mini food processor.**

RASPBERRY-RHUBARB CAKE

# Raspberry-Rhubarb Cake

SERVES 8

¾ cup all-purpose flour

¼ cup oat flour or all-purpose flour

½ teaspoon baking powder

½ teaspoon baking soda

¼ teaspoon salt

4 tablespoons butter, softened

⅔ cup sugar

▲ 1 large egg

½ teaspoon vanilla extract

½ cup low-fat buttermilk

▲ ½ cup finely chopped fresh rhubarb or frozen chopped rhubarb

▲ 2½ cups fresh raspberries

1 teaspoon confectioners' sugar

**PER SERVING** (⅛ of cake with ¼ cup berries):
183 Cal, 7 g Total Fat, 4 g Sat Fat, 0 g Trans Fat, 43 mg Chol, 252 mg Sod, 29 g Carb, 15 g Sugar, 3 g Fib, 3 g Prot, 47 mg Calc.

**5** PointsPlus value

1   Preheat oven to 375°F. Spray 9-inch round cake pan with nonstick spray.

2   Whisk together flours, baking powder, baking soda, and salt in medium bowl. With an electric mixer on medium speed, beat butter in large bowl until creamy, about 1 minute. Gradually add sugar and beat until light and fluffy, about 4 minutes. Reduce speed to low and beat in egg and vanilla.

3   Alternately add flour mixture and buttermilk to butter mixture, beginning and ending with flour mixture and beating just until blended. Gently fold in rhubarb. Pour batter into pan; spread evenly. Sprinkle top with ½ cup raspberries.

4   Bake until wooden pick inserted into center comes out clean, 35–40 minutes. Cool cake in pan on wire rack 10 minutes. Remove cake from pan and let cool completely on rack. Dust with confectioners' sugar and serve with remaining 2 cups raspberries.

**FYI**  To make your own buttermilk, add 1 teaspoon vinegar or lemon juice to ½ cup of milk and let stand at room temperature until thickened slightly, about 10 minutes. Oat flour is available in health food stores, or you can make your own by processing dry old-fashioned oats in a food processor until finely ground.

# Apricot-Cherry Clafouti

SERVES 8

▲ 5 ripe apricots, halved and pitted

▲ 1 cup fresh or frozen unsweetened cherries

½ cup sugar

3 tablespoons all-purpose flour

⅛ teaspoon salt

▲ 2 large eggs

½ cup low-fat (1%) milk

¼ cup light sour cream

1 teaspoon vanilla extract

**PER SERVING (⅛ of dessert):**
103 Cal, 3 g Total Fat, 1 g Sat Fat,
0 g Trans Fat, 57 mg Chol,
65 mg Sod, 18 g Carb, 14 g Sugar,
1 g Fib, 3 g Prot, 40 mg Calc.

**3** PointsPlus® value

1 Preheat oven to 350°F. Spray 10-inch pie plate with nonstick spray.

2 Arrange apricots, cut side up, in pie plate. Place cherries around apricots.

3 Whisk together sugar, flour, and salt in large bowl. Whisk together eggs, milk, sour cream, and vanilla in small bowl. Add egg mixture to sugar mixture and whisk until blended. Pour batter over fruit.

4 Bake until puffed and golden brown, 40–45 minutes. Cut into wedges and serve warm.

**FYI** You can substitute plums or small peaches or nectarines for the apricots in this recipe.

# Apple-Blackberry Crisp

▲ **4 large Golden Delicious apples, peeled, cored, and sliced (2 pounds)**

**3 tablespoons plus ¼ cup sugar**

**1 tablespoon lemon juice**

**1¼ teaspoons ground cinnamon**

▲ **1 cup fresh or frozen blackberries**

**¾ cup old-fashioned oats**

**½ cup whole wheat pastry flour**

**⅛ teaspoon salt**

**2 tablespoons unsalted butter, softened**

**1 tablespoon honey**

**PER SERVING (1 cup):**
170 Cal, 4 g Total Fat, 2 g Sat Fat,
0 g Trans Fat, 8 mg Chol,
37 mg Sod, 35 g Carb, 22 g Sugar,
4 g Fib, 2 g Prot, 20 mg Calc.

**5 PointsPlus® value**

**1** Preheat oven to 400°F. Spray 2-quart baking dish with nonstick spray.

**2** Stir together apples, 3 tablespoons sugar, lemon juice, and ½ teaspoon cinnamon in large bowl. Add blackberries and toss gently to combine. Transfer fruit mixture to dish.

**3** Stir together oats, flour, remaining ¼ cup sugar, remaining ¾ teaspoon cinnamon, and salt in medium bowl. With your fingers, blend in butter and honey until crumbly. Sprinkle evenly over fruit.

**4** Bake until fruit filling is bubbly and topping is light golden brown, 35–40 minutes. Let cool in pan on wire rack. Serve warm.

**FYI** A dollop of yogurt makes this fruit crisp an extra special treat (⅓ cup plain fat-free yogurt will increase the *PointsPlus* value by *1*).

# Apple-Pear Tart Tatin

SERVES 8

## CRUST

½ cup whole wheat pastry flour

½ cup all-purpose flour

¼ cup millet flour

2 teaspoons sugar

½ teaspoon salt

6 tablespoons cold unsalted butter, cut into small pieces

2 tablespoons ice water

## FILLING

▲ 3 firm ripe Bosc pears, each peeled, cored, and cut into 4 wedges (1 pound)

▲ 3 small Golden Delicious apples, each peeled, cored, and cut into 4 wedges (1 pound)

1 tablespoon lemon juice

¼ teaspoon salt

1 tablespoon unsalted butter

¾ cup sugar

1 tablespoon water

**PER SERVING** (⅛ of tart):
261 Cal, 11 g Total Fat, 6 g Sat Fat, 0 g Trans Fat, 27 mg Chol, 220 mg Sod, 44 g Carb, 26 g Sugar, 4 g Fib, 2 g Prot, 17 mg Calc.

1  To make crust, place flours, sugar, and salt in food processor and pulse until blended. Add butter; pulse until mixture is crumbly. Add water and pulse just until combined. Flatten dough into disk. Wrap and refrigerate until chilled, 2 hours.

2  To make filling, toss together pears, apples, lemon juice, and salt in large bowl. Heat butter in 9- or 10-inch cast-iron or other ovenproof heavy-bottomed skillet over medium-high heat. Add sugar and water and bring to boil. Cook, shaking pan occasionally, until syrup is golden caramel color, about 4 minutes. Remove pan from heat.

3  Starting at edge of skillet, arrange apples and pears alternately in concentric circles on sugar mixture, filling in the center with any remaining fruit. Set skillet over medium heat and cook, shaking pan occasionally until fruit is almost fork-tender, 15 minutes. Remove pan from heat.

4  Preheat oven to 400°F.

5  On lightly floured surface, roll out dough to 11-inch circle. Place dough over filling. Carefully tuck edge of dough along side of the skillet. Using sharp knife, cut 4 slits in dough. Bake until crust is golden, 40 minutes.

6  Remove skillet from oven; let cool in pan on wire rack about 10 minutes. Invert large platter on top of skillet. Quickly turn skillet upside down to unmold the tart. Serve warm or at room temperature.

**FYI**  Millet flour gives a nice crunch to this dough, similar to cornmeal. You can purchase millet in bulk in most health food markets and grind it into flour, using a clean coffee grinder or mini food processor. If you prefer, you can substitute yellow cornmeal in this recipe.

**APPLE-PEAR TART TATIN**

# Peaches Stuffed with Almond Millet

SERVES 4

▲ ½ cup millet

1 ¼ cups unsweetened almond milk

⅓ cup plus 2 teaspoons packed brown sugar

⅛ teaspoon salt

3 tablespoons dried currants

½ teaspoon pumpkin pie spice

¼ teaspoon almond extract

▲ 4 medium peaches, halved and pitted

¼ cup light sour cream

2 tablespoons sliced almonds

PER SERVING (2 stuffed peach halves, 1 tablespoon sour cream, and ½ tablespoon almonds): 290 Cal, 6 g Total Fat, 2 g Sat Fat, 0 g Trans Fat, 5 mg Chol, 147 mg Sod, 56 g Carb, 25 g Sugar, 5 g Fib, 6 g Prot, 120 mg Calc.

1 Place millet in medium saucepan and set over medium heat. Cook, stirring often, until golden brown and fragrant, about 5 minutes. Add almond milk, ⅓ cup sugar, and salt. Bring to simmer and cook, covered, until millet is tender, 25 minutes. Stir in currants, pumpkin pie spice, and almond extract.

2 Meanwhile, halve and pit peaches. If necessary, cut a thin slice off rounded side of peach halves so they sit level. Arrange peaches, cut side up, in single layer in large microwavable dish. Cover with wax paper and microwave on High until peaches are softened, 2 minutes.

3 Spoon millet mixture evenly onto peach halves; cover with wax paper and microwave on High until peaches are tender, about 2 minutes.

4 Meanwhile, stir together sour cream and remaining 2 teaspoons sugar. Top peaches evenly with sour cream mixture and sprinkle with almonds.

FYI Millet is a small round grain that is a staple in Asia, Russia, and western Africa. It has a mild, slightly nutty flavor and crunchy texture. Almond milk is made from ground almonds mixed with water. Look for it in large supermarkets in shelf-stable aseptic boxes or in the refrigerated dairy case.

# Grilled Nectarines with Bourbon Sauce

SERVES 4

UNDER 20 MINUTES

¼ cup water

¼ cup packed light brown sugar

1 tablespoon cornstarch

1 tablespoon honey

1 tablespoon bourbon

1 teaspoon unsalted butter

¼ teaspoon vanilla extract

▲ 4 nectarines, halved and pitted

1 cup reduced-fat vanilla ice cream

**PER SERVING** (2 nectarine halves, ¼ cup ice cream, 1½ tablespoons sauce: 257 Cal, 5 g Total Fat, 3 g Sat Fat, 0 g Trans Fat, 35 mg Chol, 33 mg Sod, 49 g Carb, 42 g Sugar, 2 g Fib, 4 g Prot, 71 mg Calc.

1   To make sauce, stir together water, brown sugar, cornstarch, honey, and bourbon in small saucepan until blended. Set over medium heat and cook, stirring constantly, until mixture comes to boil and thickens, about 2 minutes. Remove from heat and stir in butter and vanilla. Set aside.

2   Spray large ridged grill pan with nonstick spray and set over medium heat. Spray nectarines lightly with nonstick spray. Place in grill pan and cook until slightly softened, about 2 minutes on each side.

3   Place 2 nectarine halves in each of 4 bowls. Top each serving with ¼ cup ice cream and drizzle evenly with sauce.

# Poached Plums with Pomegranate and Port Sauce

SERVES 4

UNDER 20 MINUTES

½ cup port wine

½ cup pomegranate juice

⅓ cup sugar

1 (3-inch) cinnamon stick

4 quarter-size slices fresh ginger, peeled

▲ 4 large plums, halved, pitted, and sliced

**PER SERVING (½ cup):**
137 Cal, 0 g Total Fat, 0 g Sat Fat,
0 g Trans Fat, 0 mg Chol,
7 mg Sod, 28 g Carb, 25 g Sugar,
1 g Fib, 1 g Prot, 12 mg Calc.

**1** Combine wine, pomegranate juice, sugar, cinnamon, and ginger in medium saucepan and bring to boil over medium-high heat. Reduce heat and simmer, stirring occasionally, until mixture is reduced to ½ cup, about 8 minutes.

**2** Add plums and cook, stirring occasionally, just until fruit is tender, about 3 minutes. Transfer to bowl and let cool. Serve warm or at room temperature. Remove and discard cinnamon and ginger before serving.

**FYI** Instead of pomegranate juice, you can make this recipe using cranberry juice.

# Chocolate-Dipped Baby Bananas

SERVES 6

▲ 12 baby bananas, peeled

3 ounces semisweet chocolate, chopped

3/4 teaspoon vegetable shortening

2 tablespoons flaked sweetened coconut, toasted

**PER SERVING (2 baby bananas):**
244 Cal, 5 g Total Fat, 3 g Sat Fat, 0 g Trans Fat, 0 mg Chol, 5 mg Sod, 50 g Carb, 35 g Sugar, 3 g Fib, 3 g Prot, 0 mg Calc.

7 PointsPlus© value

**1** Line large baking sheet with wax paper. Insert wooden craft stick or short wooden skewer in one end of each banana.

**2** Combine chocolate and shortening in top of double-boiler set over simmering water and stir until melted, about 3 minutes.

**3** Working with 1 banana at a time, spoon chocolate over bananas to cover. Sprinkle bananas with coconut and place on baking sheet. Refrigerate until chocolate sets, about 20 minutes.

**FYI** If you can't find baby bananas for this recipe, use 4 regular bananas and cut each one crosswise into thirds.

# Oranges with Spiced Caramel Sauce

**SERVES 4**

2 tablespoons plus ¼ cup water

⅓ cup sugar

1 teaspoon unsalted butter

¼ teaspoon five-spice powder

▲ 4 navel or blood oranges

▲ Pomegranate seeds, for garnish (optional)

**PER SERVING (4 orange slices with 1½ tablespoons sauce):**
118 Cal, 1 g Total Fat, 1 g Sat Fat,
0 g Trans Fat, 3 mg Chol,
2 mg Sod, 30 g Carb, 24 g Sugar,
3 g Fib, 1 g Prot, 63 mg Calc.

**1** Place 2 tablespoons of the water in medium saucepan. Sprinkle sugar in an even layer in pan. Set over medium-low heat and cook, without stirring, until the mixture just begins to turn golden, about 4 minutes. Cook, swirling pan occasionally, until mixture is golden, about 1 minute.

**2** Remove saucepan from heat. Wearing long oven mitts to protect your arms and being careful to avoid any spatters, carefully pour remaining ¼ cup water down side of pan. Return saucepan to heat. Add butter and five-spice powder and cook, stirring constantly, 30 seconds longer. Remove saucepan from heat and let cool to room temperature.

**3** Meanwhile, remove peel and pith from oranges. Trim off ¼ inch from ends of each orange, then cut each orange into 4 crosswise slices. Arrange oranges evenly on 4 plates, drizzle evenly with sauce, and garnish with pomegranate seeds (if using).

**FYI** When making caramel, use a light-colored saucepan, such as stainless steel, or a light-colored enamel-coated pan so you can easily see the color of the sugar as it caramelizes and prevent overbrowning.

ORANGES WITH SPICED
CARAMEL SAUCE

# Cranberry-Ginger Fool

SERVES 4

▲ **2 cups fresh or frozen cranberries**

**³⁄₄ cup sugar**

**¹⁄₄ cup water**

**¹⁄₄ teaspoon ground ginger**

**1 teaspoon grated orange zest**

▲ **³⁄₄ cup plain fat-free Greek yogurt**

**1 cup frozen light whipped topping, thawed**

**PER SERVING** (scant 1 cup):
176 Cal, 2 g Total Fat, 2 g Sat Fat,
0 g Trans Fat, 0 mg Chol,
18 mg Sod, 41 g Carb, 33 g Sugar,
2 g Fib, 4 g Prot, 34 mg Calc.

**1** Combine cranberries, sugar, water, ginger, and orange zest in medium saucepan and set over medium heat. Bring to simmer and cook, stirring occasionally, until cranberries pop and mixture is thickened, 8 minutes. Let stand to cool to room temperature.

**2** Transfer cranberry mixture to food processor and process until smooth. Transfer to medium bowl. Stir in yogurt. Gently fold in whipped topping in 2 additions until just mixed. Cover and refrigerate at least 2 hours or up to 1 day before serving.

**FYI** A fool is a classic English dessert made with sweetened fruit puree combined with whipped cream. Tart red cranberries make this version especially appropriate to serve during the winter holidays.

SERVES 6

UNDER 20 MINUTES

1 cup part-skim ricotta cheese

$^1/_3$ cup confectioners' sugar

1 teaspoon grated lemon zest

$^1/_2$ teaspoon vanilla extract

1 cup frozen light whipped topping, thawed

▲ 3 cups pitted fresh cherries or 1 (12-ounce) bag frozen unsweetened cherries, thawed

3 tablespoons cherry or raspberry jam

8 ladyfingers, coarsely crumbled

**PER SERVING** (1 parfait):
238 Cal, 6 g Total Fat, 4 g Sat Fat,
0 g Trans Fat, 45 mg Chol,
73 mg Sod, 41 g Carb, 24 g Sugar,
2 g Fib, 7 g Prot, 130 mg Calc.

# Cherry-Ricotta Parfaits

**1** Stir together ricotta, confectioners' sugar, lemon zest, and vanilla in medium bowl until combined. Gently stir in whipped topping.

**2** Reserve 6 cherries for garnish. Stir together remaining cherries and jam in medium bowl. Alternately layer one sixth of cherry mixture, ricotta mixture, and cookies in each of 6 parfait glasses. Garnish each parfait with a cherry. Serve at once.

**FYI** You can make the parfaits even more colorful and satisfying by adding 1 cup of fresh blueberries along with the cherries.

# Honeyed Fruits with Yogurt and Coconut

SERVES 4

UNDER 20 MINUTES

2 tablespoons honey

½ teaspoon grated lime zest

1 tablespoon lime juice

▲ 2 kiwifruit, peeled and diced

▲ 1 large apple, diced

▲ 1 mango, peeled, pitted, and diced

▲ 1 navel orange, peeled and cut into sections

▲ 1 banana, sliced

2 teaspoons chopped fresh mint

▲ 4 tablespoons plain fat-free Greek yogurt

2 tablespoons flaked sweetened coconut, toasted

**PER SERVING (1½ cups):**
186 Cal, 1 g Total Fat, 1 g Sat Fat,
0 g Trans Fat, 0 mg Chol,
16 mg Sod, 45 g Carb, 34 g Sugar,
5 g Fib, 3 g Prot, 51 mg Calc.

**1** Stir together honey and lime zest and juice in large bowl. Add kiwifruit, apple, mango, orange, banana, and mint; toss to combine.

**2** Divide fruit mixture evenly among 4 bowls; top evenly with yogurt and sprinkle with coconut.

**FYI** To toast the coconut, place it in a small skillet and set over low heat. Cook, stirring frequently, until the coconut is fragrant and lightly browned, about 3 minutes. Transfer to a small plate to cool.

# Summer Fruits with Limoncello

SERVES 6

UNDER 20 MINUTES

2 tablespoons honey

2 tablespoons lemon-flavored Italian liqueur (such as Limoncello)

1 teaspoon grated lemon zest

1 tablespoon lemon juice

▲ 3 cups cubed honeydew

▲ 2 peaches, peeled, pitted, and sliced

▲ 2 cups strawberries, hulled and quartered

▲ 1 cup fresh blueberries

3 tablespoons thinly sliced fresh basil leaves

**PER SERVING** (generous 1 cup):
115 Cal, 0 g Total Fat, 0 g Sat Fat,
0 g Trans Fat, 0 mg Chol,
16 mg Sod, 27 g Carb, 20 g Sugar,
3 g Fib, 1 g Prot, 19 mg Calc.

**1** Stir together honey, liqueur, lemon zest, and lemon juice in large bowl.

**2** Add honeydew, peaches, strawberries, and blueberries; toss to combine. Serve at once, or cover and refrigerate up to 4 hours and serve chilled. Stir in basil just before serving.

**FYI** To add more colorful melon to this salad, toss in 1 cup cubed cantaloupe or seedless watermelon.

# Strawberry-Yogurt Crush with Sugared Pumpkin Seeds

SERVES 4

UNDER 20 MINUTES

**3 tablespoons raw shelled pumpkin seeds**

**1 ½ teaspoons granulated sugar**

**⅛ teaspoon salt**

**½ cup superfine sugar**

**▲ 1 (1-pound) bag frozen unsweetened strawberries**

**⅓ cup plain low-fat yogurt**

**2 tablespoons lime juice**

**1 tablespoon tequila (optional)**

**PER SERVING (1 dessert):**
156 Cal, 3 g Total Fat, 1 g Sat Fat,
0 g Trans Fat, 1 mg Chol,
88 mg Sod, 30 g Carb, 22 g Sugar,
3 g Fib, 4 g Prot, 58 mg Calc.

1 Spray small baking sheet with nonstick spray.

2 Place pumpkin seeds in small nonstick skillet. Set over medium heat and cook, stirring frequently, until seeds begin to pop, about 4 minutes. Sprinkle pumpkin seeds with granulated sugar, and cook, stirring constantly, until sugar melts and coats seeds, about 1 minute. Spread seeds on baking sheet. Sprinkle with salt and set aside to cool.

3 Meanwhile, place superfine sugar in food processor; process until very finely ground, 1 minute. Add strawberries and pulse until finely chopped. Add yogurt, lime juice, and tequila, if using, and process until smooth. Divide evenly among 4 bowls, sprinkle each with about 1 tablespoon pumpkin seeds, and serve at once.

**FYI** If fresh strawberries are available, top each serving of the dessert with a handful for a fresh and pretty garnish.

# Coconut-Lime Granita with Mango and Watermelon

SERVES 6

2 cups water

³/₄ cup sugar

¹/₄ cup light corn syrup

³/₄ cup light (reduced-fat) coconut milk

2 teaspoons grated lime zest

¹/₃ cup lime juice

¹/₈ teaspoon coconut extract

▲ 1 cup diced mango

▲ 1 cup diced seedless watermelon

PER SERVING (1 cup granita with ¹/₃ cup fruit): 147 Cal, 2 g Total Fat, 0 g Sat Fat, 0 g Trans Fat, 0 mg Chol, 13 mg Sod, 37 g Carb, 28 g Sugar, 1 g Fib, 1 g Prot, 10 mg Calc.

**1** Combine 1 cup water, sugar, and corn syrup in large saucepan and set over medium heat. Cook, stirring often, until sugar is dissolved, 2 minutes. Remove saucepan from heat and stir in coconut milk, remaining 1 cup water, lime zest and juice, and coconut extract.

**2** Pour mixture into 9 x 13-inch baking pan. Cover with foil and freeze until firm, 6–8 hours.

**3** Use a fork to scrape across surface of granita, transferring ice shards to dessert dishes. Top each serving evenly with mango and watermelon. Serve at once.

**FYI** You can toss the fruit with 2 teaspoons thinly sliced fresh basil or mint if you have it on hand. For a creamy-textured granita, you can chill the mixture and then process it in an ice-cream maker according to the manufacturer's instructions.

# Dreamy Raspberry Ice Pops

SERVES 8

▲ 1 1/2 cups fresh or frozen
raspberries

1 (6-ounce) container fat-free
raspberry yogurt

1/2 cup water

1/4 cup honey

1 1/2 teaspoons lemon juice

2 teaspoons raspberry
liqueur (optional)

**PER SERVING (1 pop):**
57 Cal, 0 g Total Fat, 0 g Sat Fat,
0 g Trans Fat, 1 mg Chol,
17 mg Sod, 14 g Carb, 12 g Sugar,
2 g Fib, 1 g Prot, 38 mg Calc.

1 Combine raspberries, yogurt, water, honey, lemon juice, and liqueur, if using, in food processor and process until smooth. Push puree through a strainer; discard seeds.

2 Pour into 8 (2-ounce) ice pop molds. Cover molds with tops and insert wooden craft sticks. Freeze until completely frozen, 6 hours or up to 1 week.

**FYI** If you don't have ice pop molds, you can make these treats in paper cups. To do so, spoon the mixture into 3-ounce paper cups and cover each cup with foil. Make a small slit in the center of the foil and insert a wooden craft stick. Freeze as directed. Remove the foil and tear away the paper cups to serve.

DREAMY RASPBERRY ICE POPS AND
COCONUT-LIME GRANITA WITH
MANGO AND WATERMELON, PAGE 309

**MULTIGRAIN BLUEBERRY SCONES, PAGE 204**

# Recipes by *PointsPlus* value

**ORANGES WITH SPICED
CARAMEL SAUCE, PAGE 302**

SEAFOOD AND WHITE
BEAN CHOWDER, PAGE 158

# Recipes that work with the
# Simply Filling technique

SPELT CRÊPES WITH RASPBERRIES
AND HONEY, PAGE 233

# Index

# Dry and Liquid Measurement Equivalents

If you are converting the recipes in this book to metric measurements, use the following chart as a guide.

| TEASPOONS | TABLESPOONS | CUPS | FLUID OUNCES |
|---|---|---|---|
| 3 teaspoons | 1 tablespoon | | 1/2 fluid ounce |
| 6 teaspoons | 2 tablespoons | 1/8 cup | 1 fluid ounce |
| 8 teaspoons | 2 tablespoons plus 2 teaspoons | 1/6 cup | |
| 12 teaspoons | 4 tablespoons | 1/4 cup | 2 fluid ounces |
| 15 teaspoons | 5 tablespoons | 1/3 cup minus 1 teaspoon | |
| 16 teaspoons | 5 tablespoons plus 1 teaspoon | 1/3 cup | |
| 18 teaspoons | 6 tablespoons | 1/4 cup plus 2 tablespoons | 3 fluid ounces |
| 24 teaspoons | 8 tablespoons | 1/2 cup | 4 fluid ounces |
| 30 teaspoons | 10 tablespoons | 1/2 cup plus 2 tablespoons | 5 fluid ounces |
| 32 teaspoons | 10 tablespoons plus 2 teaspoons | 2/3 cup | |
| 36 teaspoons | 12 tablespoons | 3/4 cup | 6 fluid ounces |
| 42 teaspoons | 14 tablespoons | 1 cup minus 2 tablespoons | 7 fluid ounces |
| 45 teaspoons | 15 tablespoons | 1 cup minus 1 tablespoon | |
| 48 teaspoons | 16 tablespoons | 1 cup | 8 fluid ounces |

| VOLUME | |
|---|---|
| 1/4 teaspoon | 1 milliliter |
| 1/2 teaspoon | 2 milliliters |
| 1 teaspoon | 5 milliliters |
| 1 tablespoon | 15 milliliters |
| 2 tablespoons | 30 milliliters |
| 3 tablespoons | 45 milliliters |
| 1/4 cup | 60 milliliters |
| 1/3 cup | 80 milliliters |
| 1/2 cup | 120 milliliters |
| 2/3 cup | 160 milliliters |
| 3/4 cup | 175 milliliters |
| 1 cup | 240 milliliters |
| 1 quart | 950 milliliters |

| LENGTH | |
|---|---|
| 1 inch | 25 millimeters |
| 1 inch | 2.5 centimeters |

| OVEN TEMPERATURE | | | |
|---|---|---|---|
| 250°F | 120°C | 400°F | 200°C |
| 275°F | 140°C | 425°F | 220°C |
| 300°F | 150°C | 450°F | 230°C |
| 325°F | 160°C | 475°F | 250°C |
| 350°F | 180°C | 500°F | 260°C |
| 375°F | 190°C | 525°F | 270°C |

| WEIGHT | |
|---|---|
| 1 ounce | 30 grams |
| 1/4 pound | 120 grams |
| 1/2 pound | 240 grams |
| 1 pound | 480 grams |

Note: Measurement of less than 1/8 teaspoon is considered a dash or a pinch. Metric volume measurements are approximate.